EMC 2

C'est à toi!

Second Edition

Activities for Proficiency

EMC Publishing, Saint Paul, Minnesota

Credits

Senior Editor
Sarah Vaillancourt

Associate Editor
Diana Moen

Teacher's Notes
Diana Moen

Electronic Design and Production Assistant
Jack Ross

Many activities in this manual originally appeared in the publication *Idées pratiques pour la classe de français*, © Mary Glasgow Publications LTD, London. We would like to thank the French Government Tourist Office, French Cultural Services, and various *Offices de Tourisme* for the information they provided in the preparation of this manual.

ISBN 0-8219-3291-8

Published by EMC Publishing
875 Montreal Way
St. Paul, Minnesota 55102
800-328-1452
www.emcp.com
E-mail: educate@emcp.com

Printed in the United States of America
1 2 3 4 5 6 7 8 9 10 XXX 12 11 10 09 08 07 06

Table of Contents

Blackline Masters Unité 3

Blackline Masters Unité 4

Blackline Masters Unité 5

Blackline Masters Unité 6

Blackline Masters Unité 7

Blackline Masters Unité 11

Introduction

The manual *Activities for Proficiency* contains reproducible blackline masters that can be used to create activities that will enhance students' proficiency in French in speaking, writing and reading. These supplemental activities correspond to the content of the units in the *C'est à toi!* textbook. The section Suggestions for Use provides ideas on how you might use the blackline masters to create activities that are stimulating and fun for your students.

The five "Cs" addressed in *Standards for Foreign Language Learning: Preparing for the 21st Century* are reflected in *Activities for Proficiency*. The activities proposed in Suggestions for Use facilitate **communication** with others, foster an understanding of the **cultures** of francophone counties, provide **connections** to other disciplines, allow for **comparisons** to be made between French and English and provide opportunities for students to participate in mulilingual **communities** at home and abroad.

Many of the activities listed in the section Suggestions for Use develop **communicative** proficiency. Students may be asked to role-play, play a game or answer specific questions. Using Blackline Master 104, students can play the roles of a server and a customer who orders from an authentic **québécois** menu. Blackline Master 70 has illustrations of musical instruments that can be used to play a card game in which students ask a group member for the card of a specific instrument to get a matching pair. With Blackline Master 13 students can conduct a survey of their partner asking if he or she has the illustrated possessions. In addition to developing oral proficiency, some of the activities help students practice writing in French. Students may be asked to fill out a form (Blackline Masters 106 and 138), write a business letter (Blackline Master 47), write original sentences (Blackline Master 152) or even a story (Blackline Masters 20 and 88).

Blackline masters that use authentic realia open a window on francophone **cultures**. To pay for restaurant bills and store purchases in role-plays, students can cut out the euro bills and coins in Blackline Master 86. Students can read e-mail by visitors to HaïtiTourisme's Internet site and answer visitors' real travel questions. By looking at Blackline Master 56 students can determine which hotel in Guadeloupe would be best for certain tourists. They can read real testimonials of tourists who have traveled in Tahiti in Blackline Master 126. To avoid cultural faux pas in Senegal, students can read Blackline Master 129.

The blackline masters encourage students to make **connections** to other subject areas, such as geography, cooking, music, art and driver's ed. Maps of the world, Europe and **le Maghreb** acquaint students with French-speaking countries around the globe (Blackline Masters 54, 123, 19 and 81) Students can read authentic French recipes (Blackline Masters 44, 45 and 125) to prepare a shopping list or actually cook a French dish for their class or family. By reading Blackline Master 83, they can become familiar with the development of **raï** music from Algeria. Students can use Blackline Master 31 as a guide for identifying which period certain paintings by Cézanne belong to. And students can simulate a French driver's ed exam using Blackline Masters 146 and 147.

When students make **comparisons** between French and English, they understand how the languages are similar and dissimilar. You may want to use Blackline Master 108 to discuss how the presence of anglo communities around Quebec have impacted the French spoken there.

The blackline masters encourage students to participate in multilingual **communities** in their classroom and abroad, often using technology. Following the instructions in Blackline Masters 95 and 128, students can send virtual postcards from francophone countries to French students in their own and other schools. If your students are interested in corresponding with a French teen, you may want them to send a letter or an e-mail to a **Maison des Jeunes et de la Culture**, such as the one highlighted in Blackline Master 72.

You will find that there are multiple uses for the blackline masters in *Activities for Proficiency*. However you decide to use them, students will benefit from these standards-based activities and become more enthusiastic French speakers while increasing their proficiency in the language.

Suggestions for Use

Unité 1

Blackline Master 1: *Invitation*
Have students brainstorm a list of reasons to have a party and write them on the board. After numbering them, have the students count off. Each student is responsible for writing an invitation for the type of party he or she drew. You may want to expand this activity and have students practice phone conversations in which they R.S.V.P. to an invitation they have received.

Blackline Master 2: *Fête*
Ask students questions about the illustration, for example, **Que font Jacques et Claire**? **Qu'est-ce qu'Annie a? Qu'est-ce qu'il y a sur la table?** You might also have students write a paragraph describing the party scene, using as many verbs and expressions as they remember from *C'est à toi! Level One*.

Blackline Master 3: *Réveillon de la Saint-Sylvestre*
Ask students to identify each course of the meal. Students might also write an invitation for this **soirée** based on the invitation on page 2 of the *C'est à toi! Level Two* textbook.

Blackline Master 4: *Jeu aux dés*
Have students working in small groups prepare two dice, one with the pronouns **je**, **tu**, **il**, **nous**, **vous** and **ils**, the other with **–er** verbs such as **décider**, **demander**, **imaginer**, **manger**, **regarder** and **rentrer**. Students in each group take turns throwing the dice and conjugating the verbs. For example, if a student throws **il** and **demander**, he or she says **Il demande**.

Blackline Master 5: *Quelle heure est-il?*
Practice telling exact time with students by asking **Quelle heure est-il**?

Blackline Master 6: *Pendule*
Have students assemble the clock. Then put students in pairs. Student A moves the hands of the clock to a certain time and asks Student B **Quelle heure est-il**? Student B responds, giving the exact time. Then have students switch roles.

Blackline Master 7: *Le calendrier et les fêtes*
Practice telling the date with students by asking questions based on the calendars, for example, **Quelle est la date de Pâques**?

Blackline Master 8: *Carte postale*
Have students write a postcard from the city of Quebec to a classmate, saying what they saw and did and what they are going to do. Students can use the postcard on page 15 of the *C'est à toi! Level Two* textbook as a model.

Blackline Master 9: *Québec*
Ask students questions about the realia, for example, **Quel président est venu au Château Frontenac**? **Quand est-ce que l'Église Notre-Dame-des-Victoires est fermée aux visiteurs?** You might have students locate these two sites on a map of Quebec, or give directions from one site to the other.

Blackline Master 10: *Carnaval de Québec*
Ask students questions about the realia, for example, **Où peut-on trouver les sculptures sur neige**? **Combien de courses est-ce qu'on peut voir?**

Blackline Master 11: *Carte de Noël*
Give students construction paper to make a Christmas card. They may draw a Christmas scene or cut out the clip art on this page and paste it on the construction paper. Students can write messages using the vocabulary at the bottom of the page.

Blackline Master 12: *Lexique de quelques mots créoles*
Working in pairs, have students present a dialogue in French that incorporates several of these Creole expressions.

Blackline Master 13: *Enquête*
Have students work with a partner to complete this survey which reviews **avoir** and negation followed by **de**.

Blackline Master 14: *Quel temps fait-il?*
Have students work in pairs to practice weather expressions. Student A points to an illustration and asks **Quel temps fait-il**? Student B answers the question, for example, **Il fait chaud**. Halfway through the illustrations, have students switch roles.

Blackline Master 15: *Bulles pour dialogues*
Have students review forming questions by writing short dialogues using the speech bubbles.

Unité 2

Blackline Master 16: *Professions et métiers I*
Have students work in pairs to practice the new vocabulary. Student A asks the profession of the people in the top row, and Student B responds. Then have students switch roles for the bottom row.

Blackline Master 17: *Grand Palais et Petit Palais*
Ask students questions about the realia, for example, **Quelle exposition est-ce que tu veux voir au Grand Palais? Quel jour est-ce que le Petit Palais est fermé?**

Blackline Master 18: *Monuments de Paris*
Have students label the map of Paris, using the expressions on the bottom.

Blackline Master 19: *L'Europe des 25*
Working with a partner, have students ask where people come from to review **venir de**. Student A points to a country on the map and asks, for example, **Yves vient d'où**? Student B identifies the country the person comes from, for example, **Il vient du Luxembourg.** Students needing more direction may want to limit themselves to the names and countries listed in the shaded area below the map.

Blackline Master 20: *Au musée d'art*
Have students write a story about the art and people in the museum.

Blackline Master 21: *Art et expositions*
Ask students questions about the realia, for example, **Quelle exposition peut-on voir au Centre Pompidou jusqu'au 8 janvier? Où est-ce qu'on peut voir une exposition de Rodin?**

Blackline Master 22: *Louvre*
Have students imagine they have just visited the Louvre with their art class. Tell them to write a paragraph in French about four of their favorite works of art. Students should include the name of the work of art, the name of the artist (where applicable), a description of the work of art and the location of the work of art.

Blackline Master 23: *Animaux I*
Have students play a communicative card game. Put students in groups of three. Give each group two copies of the grid containing the animal drawings (preferably on card stock). Then have students cut out the squares. Next they shuffle the cards (squares). The dealer deals out all the cards. Then the first student asks a group member if he or she has the animal on one of his or her cards, for example, **Est-ce que tu as un tigre**? The student who is questioned responds affirmatively or negatively: **Oui, j'ai un tigre./Non, je n'ai pas de tigre.** If the first student makes a match, he or she takes another turn. If not, the student to the right of the first student takes a turn. The student with the most pairs at the end of the game wins.

Blackline Master 24: R.E.R.
Have students practice using the R.E.R. map. Give them a place of origin and a destination and have them describe, orally or in writing, how to get from one place to another. For example, if you say **l'aéroport Charles de Gaulle—l'Étoile**, students might say: **Je suis à l'aéroport Charles de Gaulle. Je vais en direction de Saint-Rémy-les-Chevreuse. Je change à Châtelet Les Halles. Je vais en direction de Cergy Le Haut. Je descends à Charles de Gaulle Étoile.**

Blackline Master 25: *Disneyland Resort Paris*
Ask students questions about the reading **Festival Halloween Pratique**, for example, **Quelles sont les dates du Festival Halloween? Quel est le prix du passeport d'entrée pour un enfant de 12 ans?**

Blackline Master 26: *Plan de Bordeaux*
Working in pairs, have students practice giving directions from the **Office de tourisme** to certain destinations. Student A plays the role of the tourist who asks directions to a specific location. Student B plays the role of the employee at the **Office de tourisme** who tells the tourist how to get to his or her destination. Have students switch roles so they both get practice using the imperative.

Blackline Master 27: *Mots croisés*
Have students review the vocabulary of **Unité 2** by making a crossword puzzle. Have students write their clues on a separate sheet of paper under the headings **Horizontalement** and **Verticalement**. Students will need two pages of graph paper, one for the answers and one for a classmate to fill out.

Unité 3

Blackline Master 28: *Moyens de transport*
Ask students how they get from one location to another, for example, **Comment est-ce que tu vas de Miami à la Martinique**? Students should give all the possible answers, for example, **Je vais de Miami à la Martinique en bateau ou en avion.**

Blackline Master 29: *Horaire des trains I*
Ask students questions about the train schedule, for example, "When does the 7:37 train arrive in Amsterdam? What stops does the 9309 train make after Paris?"

Blackline Master 30: *Marseille*
Ask students questions about the realia, for example, **Comment s'appelle l'artiste qui a fait "Le port de Marseille"? Quelle est l'adresse du musée Cantini?**

Blackline Master 31: *Œuvre de Cézanne*
Organize a Cézanne exhibition in your classroom. Display a painting from each of Cézanne's periods and ask students to identify the period for each **tableau**.

Blackline Master 32: *Messages*
Record a different message on four cassette tapes. Then place each tape in a tape recorder. Set the tape recorders in four different locations in the classroom. Have students go to each tape recorder and listen to each message, writing down the messages on the message paper.

Blackline Master 33: *Animaux II*
Have students write in the names of the animals, including the appropriate indefinite article.

Blackline Master 34: *La ferme et ses animaux*
Have students label the parts of the farm and the farm animals.

Blackline Master 35: *Qu'est-ce qu'ils lisent?*
Ask students what people in the illustration are reading, for example, **Qu'est-ce que Mlle Latour lit**?

Blackline Master 36: *Provinces et produits de France*
Have students label the listed provinces and cities on the map.

Blackline Master 37: *Au restaurant I*
Have students write a paragraph describing the scene at the restaurant.

Blackline Master 38: *Au restaurant II*
Have students write a dialogue about one of the two tables with people at it. After you have reviewed the dialogues, have students perform them for the class.

Blackline Master 39: *Chez Jean-Paul*
Working in pairs, have students do a role-play in a restaurant. One student is the server and the other is the client. The server asks the client what he or she desires for an hors-d'œuvre, main dish, vegetable, cheese, dessert and beverage. The client selects what he or she would like to eat from the menu. You might have the client pay with euros cut out from Blackline Master 86.

Blackline Master 40: *Au Petit Galop*
This menu provides another opportunity for students to do a role-play in a restaurant. See the suggestions above.

Blackline Master 41: *Menu*
Have students plan a menu, listing several French dishes for each course. Have them write in prices for each dish using the euro.

Blackline Master 42: *Addition*
Have students playing the role of a server in activities 39 and 40 write in the client's order and total the amount of the meal before giving it to the client.

Blackline Master 43: *Léon de Bruxelles*
Tell students that this chain is opening a restaurant in their town. Their job is to translate the menu items into English for an American clientele.

Blackline Master 44: *Mousse au chocolat*
Have students make this recipe at home or in the kitchen of your Family and Consumer Sciences Department.

Blackline Master 45: *Coq au vin*
Have students make a shopping list of what they would need to buy in order to make this recipe. If they already have an ingredient at home, they do not need to include it on their shopping list.

Blackline Master 46: *Art de vivre gourmet*
Ask students to make a list of the specialties to be found in Lyon.

Blackline Master 47: *Contactez un musée d'art à Paris*
Have students read the **Lecture** section on page 147 of the textbook. Then have them follow the directions for this activity and write a business letter to a Paris art museum requesting a map and brochure. You may want to have students do this assignment in the computer lab.

Unité 4

Blackline Master 48: ***Affaires de toilette***
Name an activity that you are going to do in the bathroom, for example, **Je vais me laver la figure.** Then students, playing the role of a valet, say what toiletries they are giving you, for example, **Voici le gant de toilette et le savon, Madame.**

Blackline Master 49: ***La journée de Claire***
Ask students what Claire does at certain times of the day, for example, **Qu'est-ce que Claire fait à 7h00 du matin? Qu'est-ce que Claire fait à 9h45 du soir?** Have students respond using reflexive verbs.

Blackline Master 50: ***La journée d'Yves***
Have students write a paragraph about Yves' day, using the expressions at the bottom of the page. For oral practice, students can relate the story to their partner, using the expressions at the bottom of the page.

Blackline Master 51: ***Appareils électroménagers***
Ask students questions about these appliances, for example, **Il y a combien de versions de cet aspirateur? Que fait le Aqua-System du fer à repasser? Combien coûte le lave-vaisselle économique?**

Blackline Master 52: ***On fait le ménage chez les Dupont.***
Ask students questions about what chores the members of the Dupont family are doing, for example, **Que fait le grand-père? Qui tond la pelouse?**

Blackline Master 53: ***Corvées***
Have students play a communicative card game. Put students in groups of three. Give each group two copies of the grid containing the chores (preferably on card stock). Then have students cut out the squares. Next they shuffle the cards (squares). The dealer deals out all the cards. Then the first student asks a group member if he or she is doing a certain chore that is represented on one of his or her cards, for example, **Tu fais la lessive?** The student who is questioned answers affirmatively or negatively: **Oui, je fais la lessive./Non, je ne fais pas la lessive.** If the first student makes a match, he or she takes another turn. If not, the student to the right of the first student takes a turn. The student with the most pairs at the end of the game wins.

Blackline Master 54: ***Pays francophones***
Have students label the francophone countries and regions listed at the bottom of the map.

Blackline Master 55: ***Haïti***
Have students familiarize themselves with HaïtiTourisme's Internet site by keying in **Haïti la Sécrétairerie d'État au Tourisme.** Then, playing the role of an employee at this organisation, have them answer the cultural questions that prospective visitors of the island have posted online.

Blackline Master 56: ***La Guadeloupe***
Tell students to imagine they work for the **Office du Tourisme** in Guadeloupe. Ask them which hotel they would recommend based on different needs, for example, **Quel hôtel est-ce que tu recommandes pour une famille allemande? Quel hôtel est-ce que tu recommandes pour une femme sportive?**

Blackline Master 57: ***La Martinique***
Ask students questions about the realia, for example, **À quelle heure est-ce que le train commence l'après-midi? Quel restaurant offre une cuisine créole? Comment s'appelle le magasin qui vend des souvenirs de la Martinique?**

Blackline Master 58: ***Passé composé des verbes réfléchis***
Ask students to write a description in the **passé composé** of each illustration, using the infinitives in the margin.

Unité 5

Blackline Master 59: ***Sports I***
Ask students which sports the teens are doing in the illustrations, for example, **Qu'est-ce qu'Adja fait? Qu'est-ce que Louis et Yves font?**

Blackline Master 60: ***Sports II***
Have students use these illustrations of sports as flashcards or to play Bingo. To play Concentration, have students use another sheet of paper and make squares that each contain the name of one of these sports. Then have students cut out the squares of illustrations and the squares of words. Students mix up the squares and place them face down. The first student turns over two squares. If an illustration and a description match, the player sets the pair aside. The player with the most matching pairs wins.

Blackline Master 61: ***Roland Garros***
Ask students questions about the tennis statistics, for example, **Quel joueuses sont classées numéro 2? M. Sharapova vient d'où?**

Blackline Master 62: ***Films et télé***
Have students point to an illustration and ask their partner, **Qu'est-ce que tu regardes**? Halfway through the illustrations, have students switch roles.

Blackline Master 63: ***Sondage***
Have students fill in the survey with how they feel about each type of TV program or film in Blackline Master 62.

Blackline Master 64: ***Télé Magazine***
Ask students what TV program they are watching at a given time, for example, **Qu'est-ce que tu regardes à 23h10**? You might also have students make a graph showing the percentage of French programming that comes from the United States.

Blackline Master 65: ***Pariscope—tous les films de la semaine***
Have students make categories for the different film genres on a sheet of paper and then put the listed films under the appropriate heading. You might also ask students questions about the movie list, for example, **Combien de films américains est-ce qu'il y a? Quel est le genre du film *La Guerre des mondes*?**

Blackline Master 66: ***Tour de France***
Ask students questions about the realia, for example, **Quelle est la distance totale du Tour de France en kilomètres**? **Où est-ce que le Tour de France commence? Combien de journées de repos est-ce que les participants ont?**

Blackline Master 67: ***Opéra National de Paris***
Ask students questions about the realia, for example, **Quelles sont les dates de *Rigoletto***? **Comment s'appellent les deux opéras de Paris? Qui est le directeur de *La Veuve Joyeuse*?**

Blackline Master 68: ***Bercy***
Ask students questions about the upcoming concerts at Bercy, for example, **Quel groupe va jouer le 21 décembre?**

Blackline Master 69: ***Instruments I***
To practice **jouer de** + instrument, ask students which instrument each student is playing, for example, **De quel instrument est-ce que Guy joue**?

Blackline Master 70: *Instruments II*
Have students play a communicative card game. Put students in groups of three. Give each group two copies of the grid containing musical instruments (preferably on card stock). Then have students cut out the squares. Next they shuffle the cards (squares). The dealer deals out all the cards. Then the first student asks a group member if he or she is playing a certain musical instrument, for example, **Tu joues du piano**? The student who is questioned answers affirmatively or negatively based on whether or not he or she has the piano card in hand: **Oui, je joue du piano./Non, je ne joue pas du piano.** If the first student makes a match, he or she takes another turn. If not, the student to the right of the first student takes a turn. The student with the most pairs at the end of the game wins.

Blackline Master 71: *Passe-temps*
Have students use the illustrations as a prompt for interviewing their partner to find out which pastimes he or she enjoys, for example, **Est-ce que tu collectionnes des timbres**? Each student circles the pastimes of their partner. After the interview, you might ask students to write a paragraph summarizing their partner's pastimes, or present their findings orally to the class.

Blackline Master 72: *Maison des Jeunes et de la Culture—Evry*
Have students write to the **Maison des Jeunes et de la Culture** in Evry or another French town to find a teen with whom they can communicate. Students can send an e-mail or write a letter using the address at the top of the page. Students should begin their correspondence by saying they would like to find a pen pal, give their age, then list the pastimes they enjoy so that the personnel can match them with a comparable French teen.

Unité 6

Blackline Master 73: ***À la poste***
Have students label the illustrations. You might ask them to write a paragraph using six of the new expressions.

Blackline Master 74: ***Timbres français***
Ask students questions about the stamps, for example, **Comment s'appelle le roman de Jules Verne que le timbre commémore? Combien coûte le timbre qui commémore le bicentenaire de la bataille d'Austerlitz?**

Blackline Master 75: ***Bijoux***
Ask students which jewelry they would buy for their friend, sister, mother and grandmother, for example, **Qu'est-ce que tu achètes pour l'anniversaire de ton amie? Qu'est-ce que tu achètes pour ta mère pour la fête des Mères?**

Blackline Master 76: ***Strasbourg***
Ask students questions about the tourist information on this page, for example, **À quelle heure est-ce que la promenade en bateau sur le Rhin commence? Combien de brasseries est-ce qu'il y a à Strasbourg? Combien coûte le passeport touristique?**

Blackline Master 77: ***Bijoux et accessoires***
Ask students to describe orally the clothing, jewelry and accessories each person is wearing.

Blackline Master 78: ***Qu'est-ce qu'elles portent?***
Have students write a paragraph describing the scene and what the characters are wearing. They can also write about where the characters are going and what they will do when they get there.

Blackline Master 79: ***Objets personnels***
Have pairs of students cut out the cards, shuffle them and divide them in half. Students take turns using each object in a complete sentence, for example, **Je porte ma montre quand je vais à l'école. J'ouvre ma maison avec ma clé.**

Blackline Master 80: ***Galeries Lafayette***
Tell students what they need, for example, **Tu as besoin d'un sac à main**. Then have them identify the number indicating the part of the store they would go to.

Blackline Master 81: ***Le Maghreb***
Have students label **le Maroc**, **l'Algérie** and **la Tunisie**, as well as their capitals.

Blackline Master 82: ***Culture algérienne***
You might use this reading to assess students' reading proficiency. Have students read the article. Then have them turn over the page and on the back write the main points they remember in any order.

Blackline Master 83: ***Raï***
Direct students' reading by asking them to write down answers to specific questions that you write on the board, for example, **Où est-ce que le raï était chanté traditionnellement? Quels sont les noms de quatre chanteurs de raï?**

Blackline Master 84: ***Carte d'identité de la Tunisie***
Have students write a question for each section of the realia. Then tell students to exchange their questions with those of a classmate. The answers are returned to the writer who corrects the answers.

Blackline Master 85: ***Shopping au Maroc***
After students have read the article, give them a true/false quiz to assess their reading comprehension.

Blackline Master 86: ***Euros***
Have students cut out the euro coins and bills and use them in dialogues when paying the server or salesperson in a role-play.

Unité 7

Blackline Master 87: À *l'aéroport I*
Have students label the illustrations. You might ask them to write a paragraph using six of the new expressions.

Blackline Master 88: À *l'aéroport II*
Have students write a story about what the characters are doing, where they are going and what they will do when they get there.

Blackline Master 89: *Bagages égarés*
Tell students to pretend Air France has lost their luggage. Have them fill out the lost luggage form.

Blackline Master 90: À *la gare I*
Have students label the illustrations. You might ask them to write sentences using several of the new expressions.

Blackline Master 91: À *la gare II*
Have students write a paragraph describing the setting and telling what the people in the illustration are doing.

Blackline Master 92: *Horaire des trains II*
Ask students questions about the train schedule, for example, "When does the 7:04 train from Tours arrive in Paris? What stops does the train 8222 make after Tours?"

Blackline Master 93: *Châteaux de la Loire*
Ask students to imagine that they are documentary filmmakers whose new assignment is to profile a castle in the Loire valley. Have them write a summary for their boss of why they chose the castle they did.

Blackline Master 94: *Chenonceaux*
Ask students questions about the realia, for example, **La cheminée de la chambre porte les initiales de qui? Quand est-ce que la galerie a été un hôpital?** Make students aware of the alternate spelling of the castle before they read.

Blackline Master 95: *Envoi de cartes postales par e-mail*
Students can send a virtual postcard featuring a **château de la Loire** by following the instructions on this page.

Blackline Master 96: *Versailles*
Have students label the appropriate parts of the castle and grounds using these expressions: **les jardins, le château de Versailles, la galerie des glaces, la chapelle, la chambre de la Reine (les petits appartements).**

Blackline Master 97: *Hôtels à Versailles*
Ask students questions about the realia, for example, **Combien de chambres est-ce qu'il y a à l'Hôtel du Cheval Rouge? Quels hôtels n'acceptent pas les animaux? Combien coûte le petit déjeuner à l'Hôtel de France?**

Unité 8

Blackline Master 98: ***Lettre pour réserver une chambre d'hôtel***
Have students fill out the letter, then key it in on the computer in the computer lab. The student's address should appear on the top left of the page.

Blackline Master 99: ***Symboles des services hôteliers***
Tell students to label each square with the correct expression from the bottom of the page.

Blackline Master 100: ***Déclaration d'arrivée à l'hôtel***
Ask students to fill in the form with their personal information, pretending they are staying in a hotel in Quebec with their family.

Blackline Master 101: ***Facture d'hôtel***
Using the pricing information in Blackline Master 102 for the **Hôtel Château Laurier**, have students imagine they are the **réceptionniste** preparing a bill for a businessman who stayed at the hotel for three nights in a **chambre supérieure** from May 2-4. On the bill students should write the type of bed the client had times three.

Blackline Master 102: ***Hôtel Château Laurier***
Ask students questions about the realia, for example, **Est-ce qu'il faut payer pour utiliser un ordinateur?** **Comment s'appelle le restaurant de l'hôtel? Quel lit coûte le plus du 3 au 7 février?**

Blackline Master 103: ***Québec***
Ask students questions about the realia, for example, **Dans quel musée est-ce qu'on peut rencontrer Jacques Cartier? Dans quelle saison est-ce qu'on peut voir la Retraite et la Relève de la Garde à La Citadelle? Quel musée offre un spectacle multimédia?**

Blackline Master 104: ***Aux Anciens Canadiens***
Tell students this restaurant in Quebec is known for its **spécialités québécoises**. First, have students acquaint themselves with the menu items. Then, working with a partner, have students play the roles of a server and client. To find out what the restaurant offers for hors-d'œuvres, beverages and desserts, have students key **Restaurant Aux Anciens Canadiens** using their favorite search engine. Then tell them to click on **Menu**.

Blackline Master 105: ***Sainte-Anne-de-Beaupré***
Ask students questions about the history of the basilica, for example, **Qui a consacré la basilique actuelle**?

Blackline Master 106: ***Auberges de jeunesse***
First, ask students questions about the **auberges de jeunesse** in Paris, for example, **L'auberge de jeunesse Léo Lagrange est près de quelle station de métro?** **Quelle est l'adresse de l'auberge de jeunesse Le d'Artagnan?** Then have students fill out the registration form for FUAJ membership.

Blackline Master 107: ***Fiche d'auberge de jeunesse***
Have students pretend they are signing in at an **auberge de jeunesse** in France and need to complete the registration form.

Blackline Master 108: ***Expressions québécoises***
Working with a partner, have students prepare a role-play using several of the listed vocabulary words and expressions. You might have a class discussion about how the presence of anglo communities around Quebec has impacted the vocabulary and expressions in that province.

Blackline Master 109: ***Place Ville-Marie***
Ask students questions about the list of shops and restaurants at the **Place Ville-Marie**, for example, **Où est-ce que tu vas pour acheter une bague en argent? Quel restaurant est un fast-food américain?** Sometimes several answers are possible.

Blackline Master 110: ***Petit déjeuner***
First, have students label the breakfast foods at the top of the page. Then, ask students to write a paragraph about the couple eating breakfast. Students can include where they are, what they are eating and what they are talking about. Your creative students might want to write a poem in the **passé composé** using Prévert's "Déjeuner du matin" as a model.

Blackline Master 111: ***Restauration à Montréal***
Ask students questions about the restaurants, for example, **Où est-ce que tu emmènes ton ami(e) pour la Saint-Valentin? Quels deux restaurants servent des repas végétariens? Quelles cartes de crédit est-ce qu'ils ont au Canada que nous n'avons pas aux États-Unis?**

Blackline Master 112: ***Festival International de Jazz de Montréal***
First, have students scan the reading and make a list of the names for players of certain instruments, for example, **guitariste, saxophoniste, harmoniciste, batteur, trompettiste** and **pianiste**. Then ask them questions about the musicians and groups, for example, **Quel est l'album le plus récent de The Robert Cray Band? Quelle est la date du concert de The New Montreal Jazz Collective?**

Unité 9

Blackline Master 113: *Professions et métiers II*
Ask students the professions of the people in the illustrations, for example, **Quelle est la profession de Mme Delrieu**?

Blackline Master 114: *Curriculum vitae*
Have students imagine that they are looking for a summer job in France. Have them fill out the résumé form. You might ask students to reenter the information on the computer and have them attach a photo, which is standard practice in France.

Blackline Master 115: *Isabelle Adjani*
Have students create a **filmographie** for Isabelle Adjani, listing the title, year and director for each film that is mentioned in the reading. Since the reading only includes films up to 1994, you might ask students to key "filmographie Isabelle Adjani" using their favorite search engine in order to include her most recent films.

Blackline Master 116: *Jeanne d'Arc*
Ask students questions about the reading, for example, **Quelle est l'adresse de la "Tour de la Pucelle"**? **Quelle partie du corps de Jeanne d'Arc n'a pas brûlé?** To use the map, ask students to tell you which streets they would take to follow the route the executioner took when he threw Jeanne d'Arc's ashes in the Seine (see legend).

Blackline Master 117: *Rouen*
Ask students questions about the realia, for example, **Quelles sont les fêtes en décembre**? **À quelle heure est-ce que le marché à la place du Vieux-Marché ouvre?**

Blackline Master 118: *L'imparfait*
Before students take the unit test, have them review the formation and uses of the imperfect using this sheet.

Blackline Master 119: *François Truffaut*
Ask students questions about Truffaut's life and career, for example, **À quel âge est-ce que Truffaut a quitté l'école**? **Avec quels acteurs et actrices célèbres est-ce qu'il a travaillé?**

Blackline Master 120: *Les Invalides*
Ask students questions about the reading, for example, **En quelle année est-ce qu'on a commencé l'église du Dôme**? **Qu'est-ce que le Musée de l'Armée couvre?**

Blackline Master 121: *Adjectives*
Ask students to describe the illustrated people, for example, **Comment est Mme Dupont**?

Blackline Master 122: *Carnet intime de Patricia Kaas*
Ask students questions about the **carnet** that acquaints students with Patricia Kaas. Then have students make a similar **carnet** in French for their favorite American singer. You might have students e-mail the **carnet** that they create to a francophone key pal.

Unité 10

Blackline Master 123: ***Le monde francophone***
Have students color the French-speaking countries on the map.

Blackline Master 124: ***Restaurants à Fort-de-France***
Ask students questions about the restaurants, for example, **Quels restaurants servent des repas créoles? Où est-ce qu'on peut avoir une glace?**

Blackline Master 125: ***Recette martiniquaise***
Have students make a shopping list of the ingredients needed to make this dish. Any ingredients they already have at home do not need to be included on the list.

Blackline Master 126: ***Témoignages de Tahiti***
Ask students which travelers did certain things, for example, **Qui a planifié son voyage à la Maison de Tahiti à Paris? Qui a fait de la plongée sous-marine?**

Blackline Master 127: ***Présentation générale de la Guyane française***
Ask students questions about the reading, for example, **Où la Guyane française est-elle située? Quand la Guyane française est-elle devenue un département français?**

Blackline Master 128: ***MadagasCartes***
Have students follow the directions for sending a virtual postcard from Madagascar to a French student in their school or another school. If the Internet site fails, key "Madagascar cartes postales virtuelles," using your favorite search engine.

Blackline Master 129: ***Culture sénégalaise***
Ask students questions about the reading, for example, **Comment est-ce qu'on dit "Bonjour" au Sénégal? Quelles provisions est-ce qu'on ne doit pas acheter le soir?**

Blackline Master 130: ***Île de Gorée***
Ask students questions about the reading, for example, **Quels pays ont occupé cette île? Quel musée est-ce que tu voudrais visiter?** If your students are interested in taking a virtual tour of the **Maison des esclaves**, have them go to this Internet site: http://webworld.unesco.org/goree/fr/visit.shtml.

Blackline Master 131: ***Fêtes en Côte-d'Ivoire***
Ask students questions about the reading, for example, **Pour quelle fête est-ce qu'il y a un grand bal costumé? Quelle fête est basée sur la légende de Bidyo? Pour quelle fête est-ce qu'il y a des sacrifices?**

Blackline Master 132: ***Voyagez en Côte-d'Ivoire***
Based on the prices listed in the reading, have students prepare a budget for a one-week stay in the **Côte-d'Ivoire**.

Blackline Master 133: ***Continents et masses d'eau***
Have students label the continents and bodies of water on the map in French.

Blackline Master 134: ***Chartres***
Ask students questions about the realia, for example, **Combien d'habitants est-ce qu'il y a à Chartres? Chartres est jumelée avec quelle ville en Angleterre? Quelle spécialité chartraine voudrais-tu goûter?**

Blackline Master 135: ***Animations organisées par l'Office de Tourisme de Chartres***
Ask students questions about the realia, for example, **Où est-ce qu'on peut entendre l'orgue pendant les Soirées Estivales? D'où est-ce qu'on part pour la visite guidée de la ville médiévale?**

Blackline Master 136: *Plages de Cannes*
Ask students questions about the different beaches, for example, **Qui est le directeur de Zénith Plage? Quelle plage offre un buffet provençal?**

Blackline Master 137: *Ici Langue: Institut de Français*
Ask students questions about the language school, for example, **Il faut avoir quel âge pour aller à Ici Langue? Quel est le cours le plus facile? Quelles sont les possibilités d'hébergement?**

Blackline Master 138: *Fiche d'inscription*
Ask students to fill out the registration form for **Ici Langue**. Students should make choices based on the information in Blackline Master 137.

Unité 11

Blackline Master 139: *Problèmes*
Ask students to label the illustrated societal problems.

Blackline Master 140: *Manchettes*
Ask students to hypothesize about these newspaper headlines and tell you what each article would probably be about.

Blackline Master 141: *Les Verts*
Have students make slogans for buttons or posters that incorporate some of Antoine's ideas for preserving the environment.

Blackline Master 142: *SIDA*
Ask students questions about the reading, for example, **Que signifie la "S" du mot SIDA? Quelles sont les deux armes de la lutte contre le SIDA?**

Blackline Master 143: *Taux de chômage par région 2005*
Have students transfer the percentages in the grid to a bar graph.

Blackline Master 144: *Expressions de la route*
Ask students to label the driving illustrations.

Blackline Master 145: *Catégories de permis*
Ask students questions about the categories of French vehicle permits, for example, **À quel âge peut-on conduire un cyclomoteur? De quel permis a-t-on besoin pour conduire une voiture?**

Blackline Masters 146 and 147: *Test du Code de la Route*
Have students test their knowledge of the French **Code de la Route** by answering four sample test questions. To learn about driving regulations in France or to take a complete test online, students can key in "code de la route" using their favorite search engine.

Blackline Master 148: *Twingo de Renault*
Ask students questions about the Twingo, for example, **Où est-ce qu'on peut ranger ses affaires? Quelle est la durée de la garantie anti corrosion?**

Blackline Master 149: *Signalisation routière internationale*
Have students work with a partner to identify the meaning of each road sign. Students can check their work by looking at road signs online. Have them key "La Sécurité Routière," using their favorite search engine.

Blackline Master 150: *À la station-service I*
Have students label each illustration, then use several expressions in original sentences.

Blackline Master 151: *Parties de la voiture*
Ask students to label the parts of the illustrated car using the expressions at the bottom of the page.

Blackline Master 152: *À la station-service II*
Have students write a complete sentence to describe what Henri is doing in each illustration.

Blackline Master 153: *Carte TOTAL Le Club*
Ask students questions about membership to **Carte TOTAL Le Club**, for example, **Qu'est-ce que vous recevez avec 10 litres de carburant? Comment est-ce que TOTAL vous aide quand vous tombez en panne?**

Blackline Master 154: *Garage*
Ask students questions about the garage ad, for example, **Si tu avais une Mercedes, est-ce que la Carrosserie Sayo pourrait la réparer? Si tu as une question pour le mécanicien, comment peux-tu le contacter?**

Invitation

....

Tu es invité(e) à une fête géniale

le ....

à .... ***heures***

Adresse: ....

....

....

RSVP: ....

Fête

Réveillon de la Saint-Sylvestre

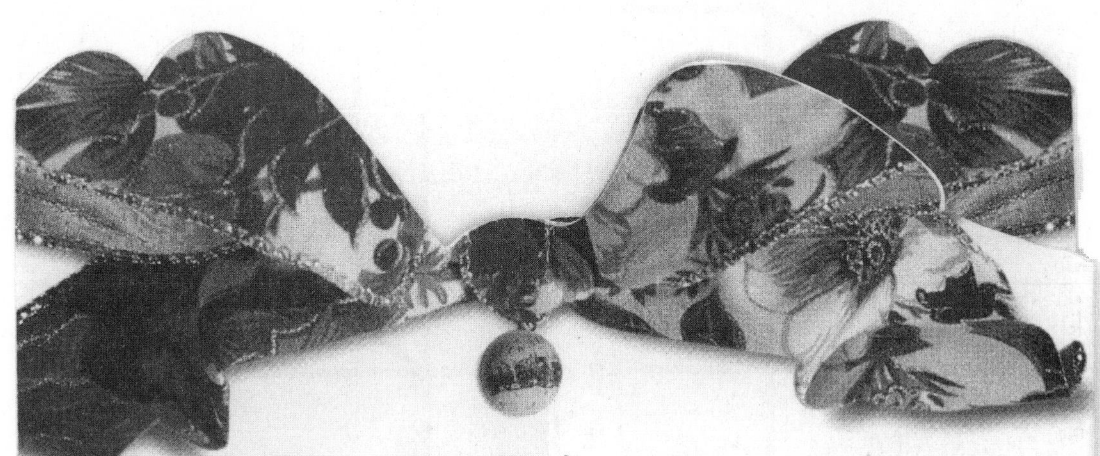

Réveillon St. Sylvestre 105,19€ TTC

champagne, cotillons et animation disc-jockey

Cocktail Clément

~ ~ ~

Petites St Jacques en coquille

sur un crémeux de crustacés au gingembre

~ ~ ~

Duo de saumon frais et fumé

dans un feuilleté doré

beurre blanc battu aux herbes et safran

~ ~ ~

Magret d'oie poêlé au pain d'épices

galette de patates douces aux châtaignes

fricassée de champignons et bananes frites

jus brun au vieux Porto

~ ~ ~

Quenelle de Brie de Meaux sur toast

petite salade d'hiver aux noisettes

~ ~ ~

Forêt noire enneigée aux griottes

crème vanillée au caramel de cerises

~ ~ ~

Fin moka et mignardises

~ ~ ~

Champagne Jeanmaire brut "Château Malakoff" à discrétion

Eaux minérales (Vittel ou San Pellegrino)

L'abus d'alcool est dangereux pour la santé.

Jeu aux dés

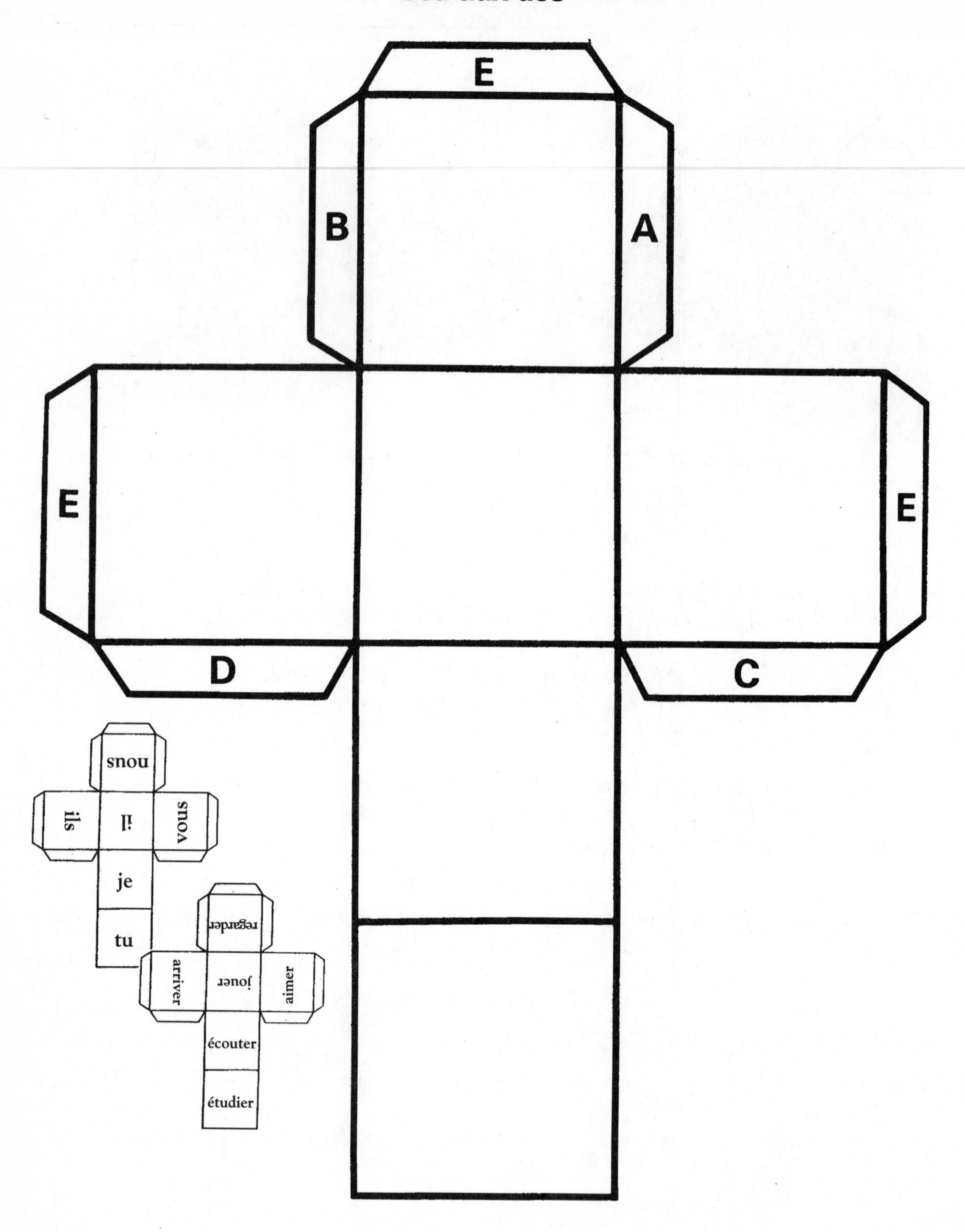
E
B
A
E
E
D
C
snou
ils
li
snov
je
tu
regarder
arriver
jouer
aimer
écouter
étudier

Quelle heure est-il?

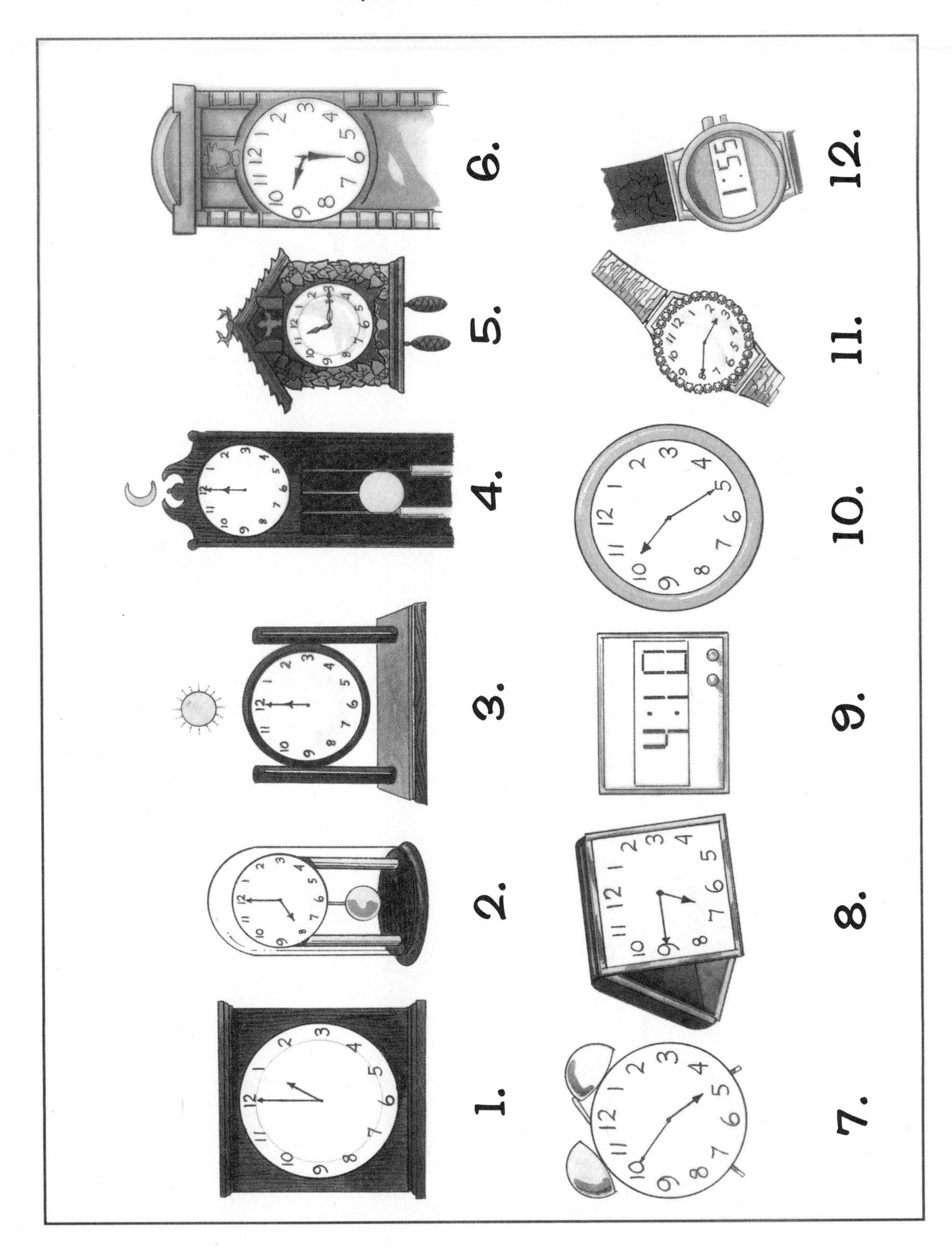

Pendule

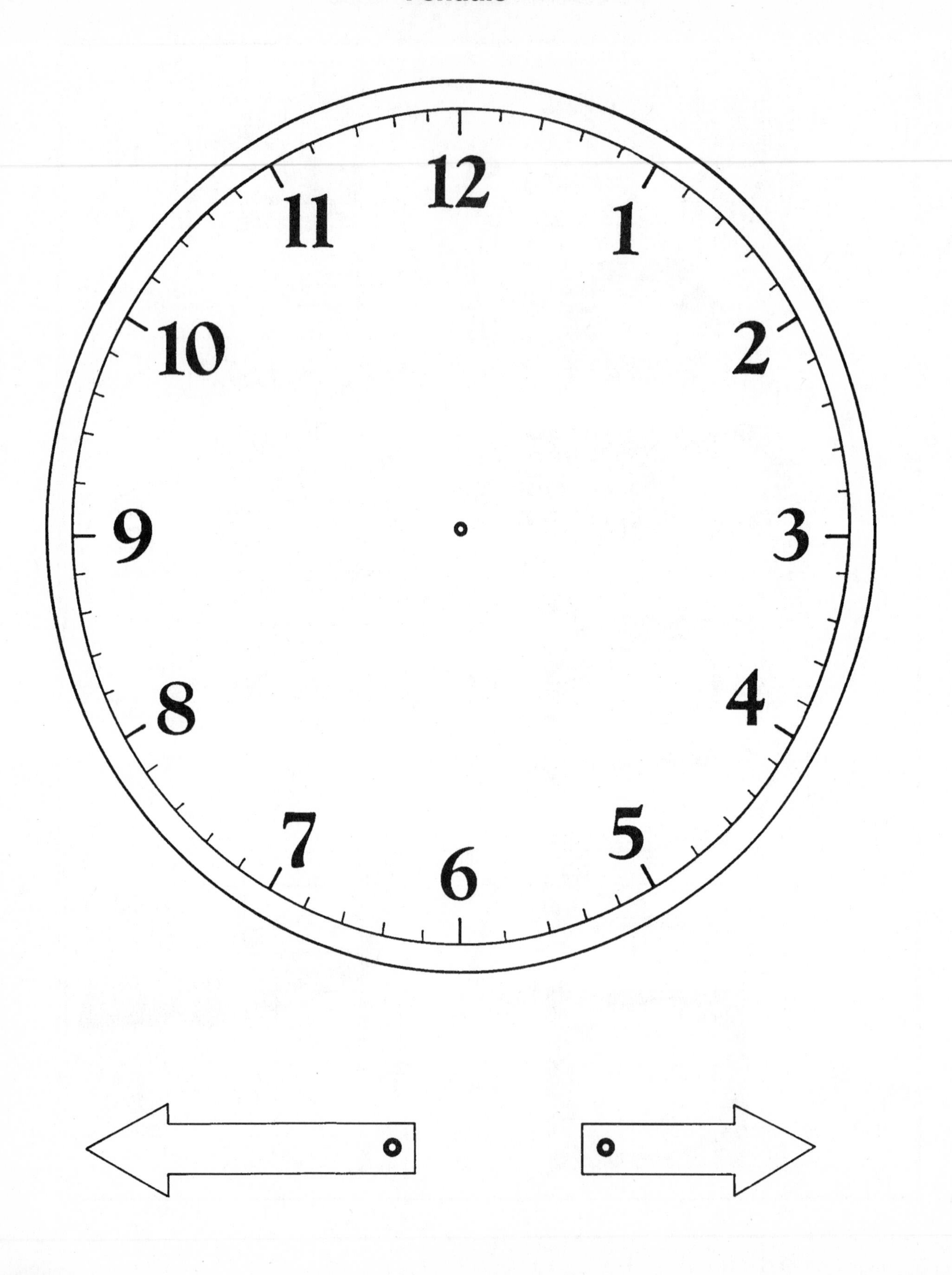

Le calendrier et les fêtes

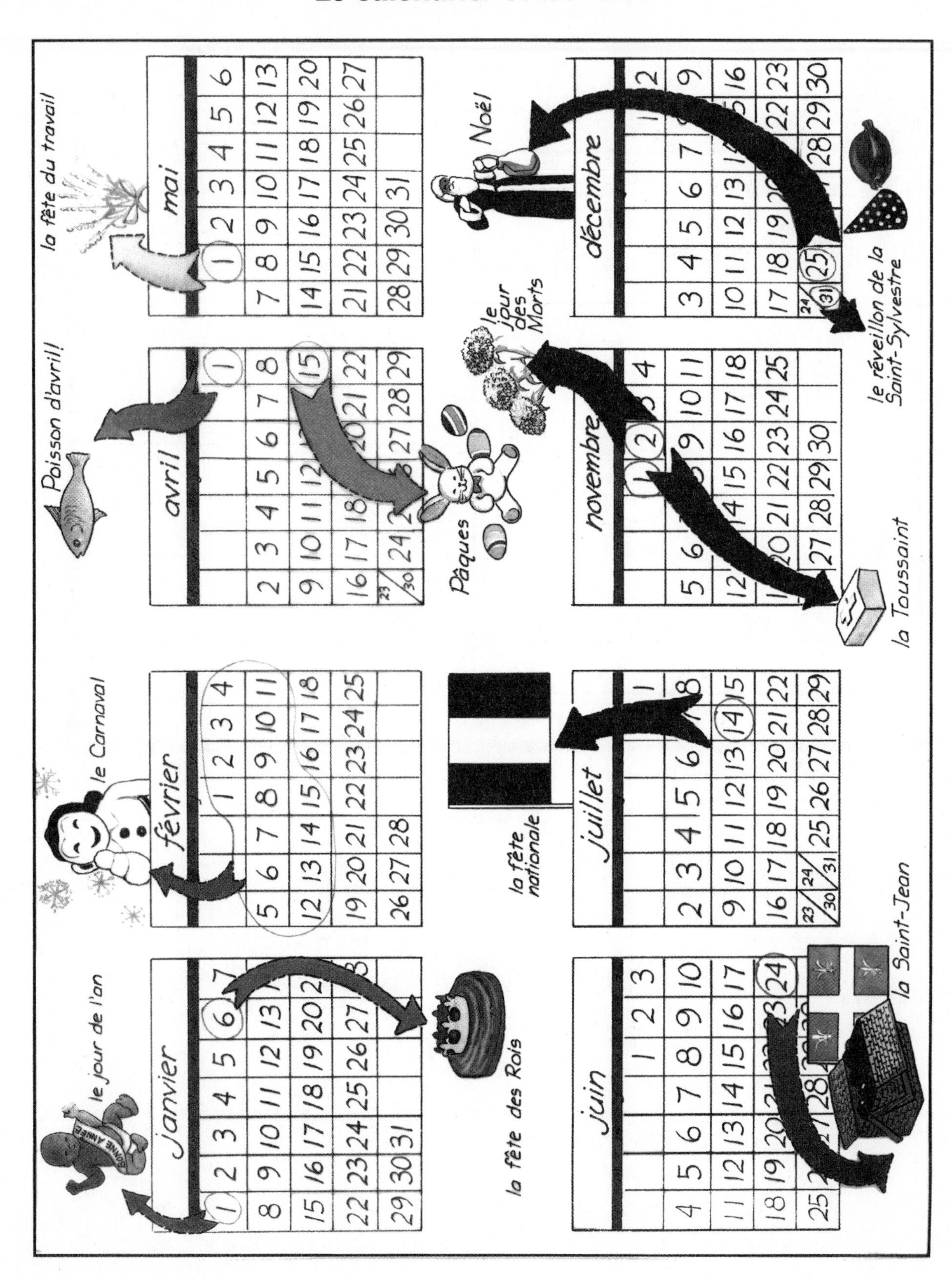

Carte postale

Québec

Château Frontenac

Cet hôtel connu mondialement a célébré son centenaire en 1993. Il doit son nom au comte de Frontenac, illustre gouverneur de la Nouvelle-France. Inaugurée en 1893, cette imposante construction a été complétée par l'addition d'une tour centrale en 1924. Deux conférences historiques, en 1943 et 1944, y réunirent Franklin Roosevelt et Winston Churchill, invités du premier ministre canadien MacKenzie King. **Visites guidées** du Château Frontenac, par un personnage de la fin du XIXe siècle. Imprégnez-vous de l'ambiance du célèbre Château centenaire. Départ à l'heure, durée de 50 minutes. **Horaire**: du 1er mai au 15 octobre, tous les jours, 10 h à 18 h. Du 16 octobre au 30 avril, samedi et dimanche, 13 h à 17 h. Visite pour groupe (15 personnes et plus) en tout temps sur réservation. **Entrée**: adultes: 6,95 $; ainés: 5,50 $; enfants (6 à 16 ans): 4,79 $. Information et réservations: Anne Géry (418) 691-2166. Tarifs spéciaux pour groupes.

Église Notre-Dame-des-Victoires

32, rue Sous-le-Fort, Québec G1K 4G7 (418) 692-1650

Érigée en 1688, c'est la plus vieille église en pierre en Amérique du Nord. Incendiée lors des bombardements de 1759, elle fût restaurée à deux reprises. Intérieur remarquable. Dans l'église, un Ex-voto représentant un modèle réduit du Brézé, vaisseau qui transporta le marquis de Tracy et les soldats du régiment de Carignan en Nouvelle-France en 1664. **Horaire**: tous les jours; 10 h à 16 h 30. Fermé lors des mariages, des baptêmes et des funérailles. Du 1er mai au 15 octobre, 9 h 30 à 16 h 30: **visites guidées** en français et en anglais. **Entrée gratuite.**

Carnaval de Québec

Les activités

Lorsque la neige envahit la Vieille Capitale, la ville revêt des airs de fête et nous présente ses jeux d'hiver. Voici les grands classiques du Carnaval qui reviennent à chaque année pour nous divertir.

Défilés de nuit

Les défilés de nuit du Carnaval en mettent plein la vue et les oreilles aux milliers de spectateurs, qui chaque année assistent à cette manifestation haute en couleurs.

Sculpture sur neige

Place Desjardins se transforme en un gigantesque musée à ciel ouvert où des sculpteurs de toutes les régions du monde viennent donner vie aux blocs de neige.

Course en canot

La course en canot, une compétition légendaire, se tient depuis la première édition du Carnaval. Chaque année, plusieurs équipes s'affrontent dans une traversée mouvementée du Fleuve entre Québec et Lévis.

La Grande virée

Personne ne voudra manquer la course d'attelages de chiens. La Grande virée est une activité typiquement nordique, qu'un tapis de neige rend féerique.

La Classique

Plus qu'un sport, la Classique de ski de fond est un mode de vie et une façon de se déplacer dans les pays nordiques. Cette activité se déroule chaque année sur les Plaines d'Abraham.

Le Bain de neige

Pour les braves ou encore pour ceux qui veulent se donner de grands frissons, rien de mieux qu'un vivifiant Bain de neige... en maillot de bain!

Course de tacot

Les plus beaux tacots dévalent la Côte de la Fabrique du Vieux-Québec. L'originalité, l'ingéniosité et la vitesse sont à l'honneur. Un spectacle divertissant!

Carte de Noël

meilleurs vœux   bonne année

pleine de joie   Joyeux Noël   de bonheur

pour une bonne et heureuse année

pour la nouvelle année   je te souhaite

Lexique de quelques mots créoles

ACCRAS : Petits beignets frits, aux poissons ou aux légumes ● **ANOLI :** Petit lézard vert ● **AJOUPA :** Petit abri recouvert de feuillage ● **BLAFF :** Méthode de cuisson au court-bouillon pour les poissons ou les crustacés ● **BAKOUA :** Petit arbre fibreux qui sert à tresser les chapeaux "bakouas", trés haut et large à la base ● **BÉKÉ :** Créole blanc ● **BETE À FEU :** Luciole ● **BLANC MANGER :** Crème dessert à base de coco ; de lait et de gélatine ● **BOUQUET GARNI :** Persil, oignon pays, thym, feuilles de bois d'inde, ou feuilles de laurier ● **CALALOU :** Soupe à base d'herbes, légumes, crabe ou cochon ● **CHABINE, CHABIN :** Personne de couleur, au teint et yeux clairs ● **CHADEC :** Gros pamplemousse ● **CHATROU :** Poulpe (pieuvre) comestible ● **CHIQUETAILLE DE MORUE :** Morue grillée, "déchiquetée" servie en vinaigrette ● **CHRISTOPHINE :** Légume (salade, sauté ou en gratin) ● **CIRIQUE :** Petit crabe ● **COLOMBO :** Viandes, volailles ou poissons au curry très épicés ● **COROSSOL :** Fruit des Antilles ● **DIFÉ :** Relevé et pimenté ● **FEROCE :** Mélange d'avocat, morue, farine de manioc et piment ● **GIRAUMON :** Potiron ainsi nommé aux Antilles ● **IGNAME :** Tubercule (légume) ● **LAMBI :** Gros coquillage comestible ● **LIME :** Citron vert ● **MANCELINIER :** Arbre dangereux de part sa sève et ses fruits (petites pommes vertes) ● **MANICOU :** Opossum ● **MATOUTOU :** Fricassée de crabes de terre ● **MATOUTOU FALAISE :** Mygale, grosse araignée vénéneuse ● **MIQUELON :** Expression de pêcheurs , aller hors de vue des côtes ● **OUASSOU :** Nom donné à l'écrevisse en Guadeloupe ● **PATÉ EN POT :** Soupe épaisse faite d'abats et de légumes ● **PISQUETTE :** Minuscule poisson de mer que l'on prépare en touffée ou en accras ● **PITT :** Arènes pour les combats de coqs ou de mangoustes ● **QUIMBOIS :** Mauvais sort ● **RAVET :** Sorte de gros cafard ● **SAVANE :** Plateau herbeux ● **SOUDON :** Sorte de palourde ● **SHRUBB :** Liqueur à base d'oranges macérées dans du rhum ● **SOUSKAI :** Macération de sel, ail et citron vert ● **TAMARIN :** Fruit aux vertus laxatives dont on mâche la pulpe peu abondante ● **TI-BO :** Baiser affectueux ● **TI-NAIN :** Bananes à consommer après cuisson comme des légumes ● **TITIRI :** Larve marine comestible ● **TOUFFÉE :** Cuisson à l'étouffée ● **TOULOULOU :** Crabe rouge-orangé ● **VIDE :** Défilé populaire (par exemple pour Carnaval) ● **VONVON :** Gros bourdon ● **YEN-YEN :** Petit moustique ● **Z'HABITANT :** Grosse écrevisse ● **ZOMBI :** Fantôme, esprit ● **ZOUK :** Fête très appréciée aux Antilles. Musique antillaise très rythmée.

Enquête

You're conducting a survey to find out if your partner has the following objects.

Modèle: —As-tu un vélo?
—Oui, j'ai un vélo.
ou
—Non, je n'ai pas de vélo.

Circle the objects your partner has, then list those objects that your partner has and doesn't have at the bottom.

Mon ami(e) a:

____
____
____
____
____
____
____

Mon ami(e) n'a pas:

____
____
____
____
____
____
____

Quel temps fait-il?

il fait beau	il fait du brouillard	il y a de l'orage
il fait chaud	il fait du soleil	il pleut
il fait froid	il fait du vent	il gèle
il fait mauvais	il y a des nuages	il neige

Bulles pour dialogues

Professions et métiers I

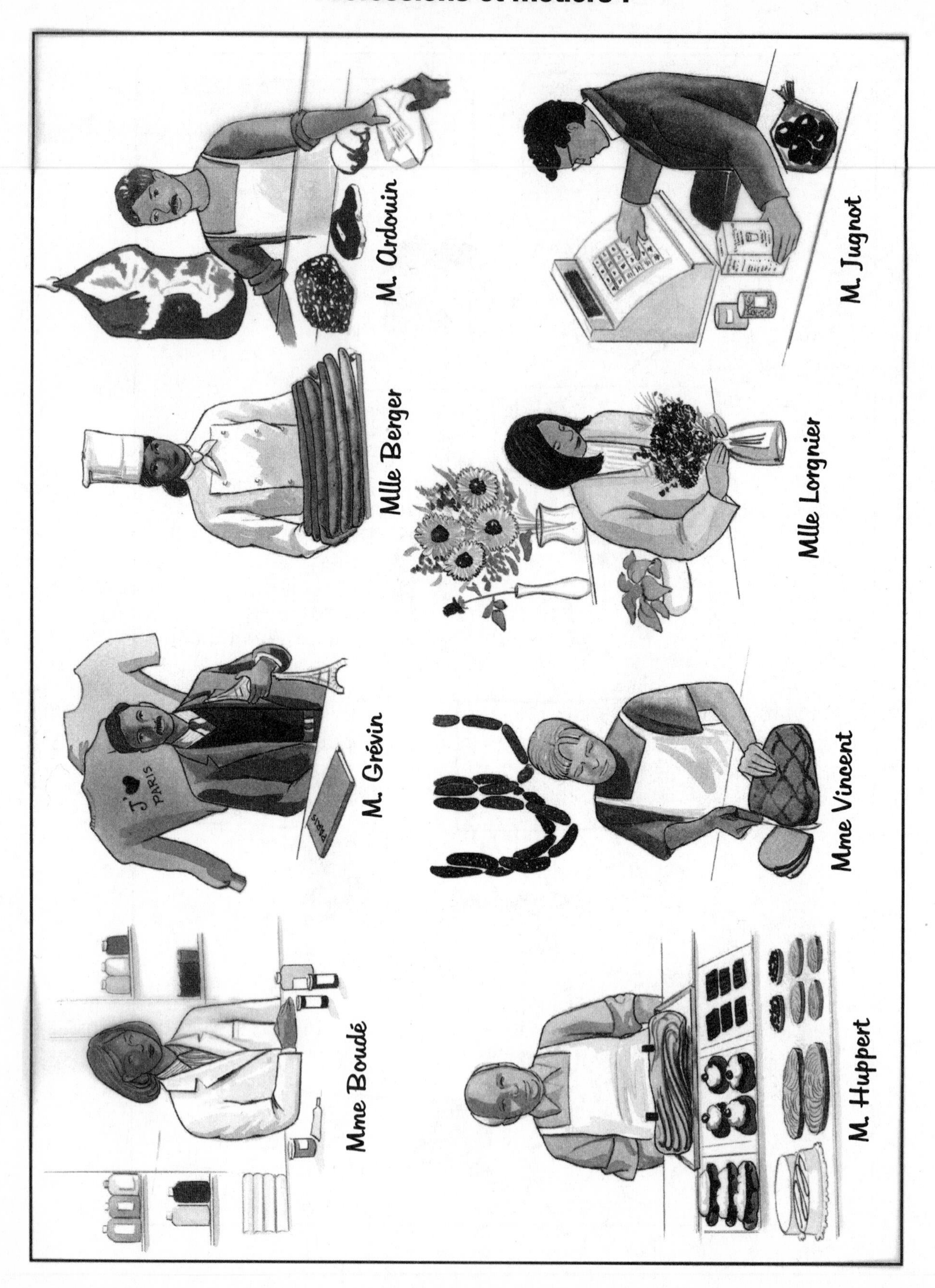

Grand Palais et Petit Palais

MUSÉES

GRAND PALAIS, (Galeries nationales du Grand Palais), 3, av. du Gal Eisenhower, square J. Perrin (8e). Mº Champs-Élysées Clémenceau ou Franklin-Roosevelt. 01.44.13.17.17. Rens. carte Sésame: 01.44.13.17.47. Tlj (sf Mar) de 10h à 20h (caisses jsq 19h15), Mer de 10h à 22h (caisses jsq 21h15). **Fermature exceptionnelle le 31 décembre à 17h. Entrée sans résa. à partir de 13h:** 7,62 €; TR et Lun: 5,34 €. **Entrée avec résa. de 10h à 13h:** 8,54 €; TR (Lun uniquement): 6,25 €. **Modalités de résa:** Fnac, Virgin, Carrefour, Printemps-Haussmann, Office de tourisme de Paris (127, av. des Champs-Élysées), par Minitel 3615 Billetel ou 3615 Fnac (0,34 €/mn), par téléphone au 08.92.68.46.94. (numéro surtaxé). Visites Gpes: 01.44.13.17.10. Audioguide français, anglais, allemand: 4,57 €. Expositions: **«Méditerranée. De Courbet à Matisse».** L'exposition réunit les œuvres des peintres de la seconde moitié du XIXe siècle qui se sont largement inspirés des paysages méditérranéens. Jusqu'au 15 janvier. **«Visions du futur. Une histoire des peurs et des espoirs de l'humanité».** Près de deux cents œuvres illustrent la représentation du futur à travers le monde et l'histoire. Jusqu'au 1er janvier.

PETIT PALAIS, Av. W. Churchill (8e). Mº Champs-Élysées Clémenceau. 01.42.65.12.73. Tlj (sf Lun et fêtes) de 10h à 17h40. Jeu jsq 20h. Ent: 4,12 €; TR: 2,21 €. Exposition temporaire: 6,10 €: TR: 4,57 €. **Collections du musée, peintures, orfèvrerie, émaux, sculptures de la Renaissance à 1925.** Expositions: **«Chine: la gloire des empereurs».** Près de 200 pièces découvertes lors de fouilles de sépultures ou de sites culturels présentent une nouvelle vision des premières dynasties chinoises. Jusqu'au 28 janvier. **«Paul Belmondo, Le dessin pour la passion».** L'œuvre graphique du sculpteur à travers une sélection de dessins, aquarelles et sanguines choisis parmi les 500 pièces appartenant à sa famille. Jusqu'au 21 janvier.

Monuments de Paris

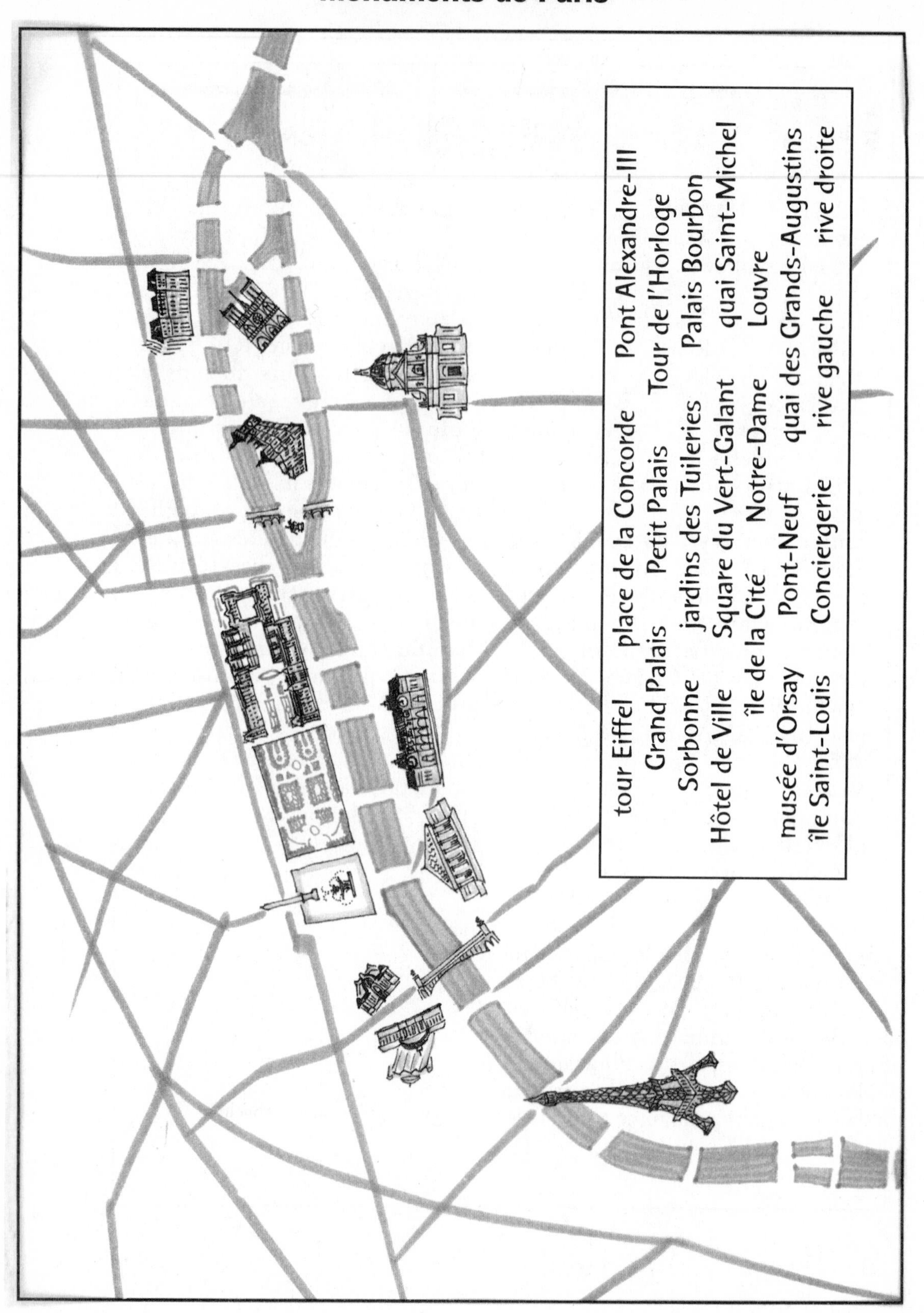

L'Europe des 25

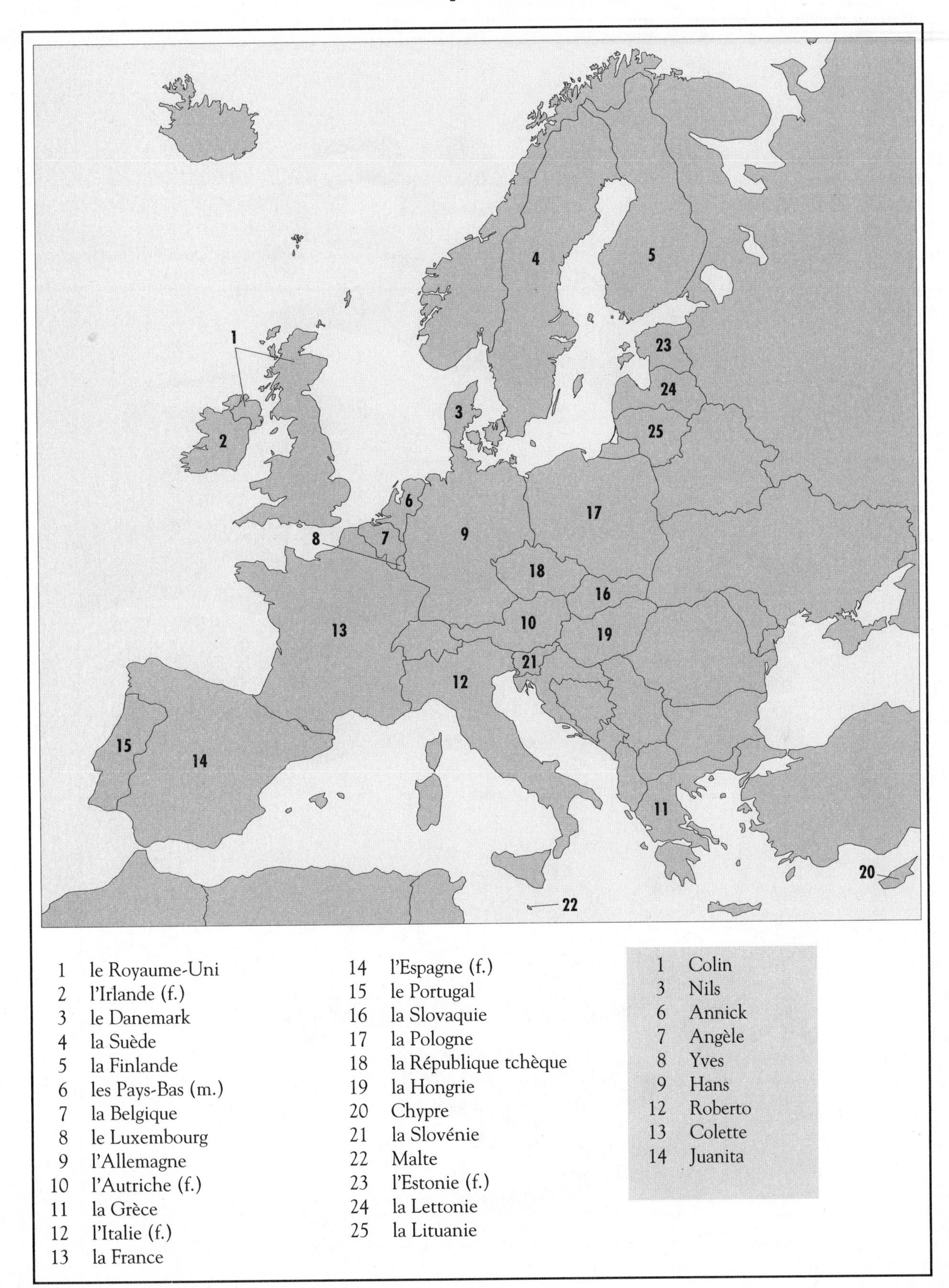

1 le Royaume-Uni
2 l'Irlande (f.)
3 le Danemark
4 la Suède
5 la Finlande
6 les Pays-Bas (m.)
7 la Belgique
8 le Luxembourg
9 l'Allemagne
10 l'Autriche (f.)
11 la Grèce
12 l'Italie (f.)
13 la France
14 l'Espagne (f.)
15 le Portugal
16 la Slovaquie
17 la Pologne
18 la République tchèque
19 la Hongrie
20 Chypre
21 la Slovénie
22 Malte
23 l'Estonie (f.)
24 la Lettonie
25 la Lituanie

1	Colin
3	Nils
6	Annick
7	Angèle
8	Yves
9	Hans
12	Roberto
13	Colette
14	Juanita

Au musée d'art

Art et expositions

Art & Exhibitions

Until 1 Jan Visions du Futur
Grand Palais, 3 av du Général-Eisenhower, 8th (01.40.13.48.00). Mº Champs-Elysées-Clemenceau. **Open** Mon, Wed-Sun 10am-8pm (Wed till 10pm). **Tickets** 7,62€/8,54€ 10am-1pm with reservation.
Subtitled 'fears and hopes of humanity', this millennial show mixes apocalyptic visions and Utopias from all periods from Antiquity and the Renaissance to a new installation by Ilya Kabakov.

Until 8 Jan Au-delà du Spectacle
Centre Pompidou, 4th (01.44.78.12.33). Mº Hôtel de Ville/RER Châtelet-Les Halles. **Open** Mon, Wed-Sun 11am-9pm. **Admission** 7,62€
A dynamic and dynamising investigation into the fascination contemporary artists have with entertainment, tinseltown, cartoon heroes and popular culture, includes Koons, McCarthy, Joseph, Sechas, Ray and a fab 3D video by Mariko Mori.

Until 21 Jan Morellet
Jeu de Paume, 1 pl de la Concorde, 8th (01.47.03.13.25). Mº Concorde. **Open** Tue noon-9.30pm; Wed-Fri noon-7pm; Sat-Sun 10am-7pm. **Admission** 4,57€
Paintings and neons by the French artist who since the 50s has been involved in a rigorous formal investigation and geometrical abstraction, including a new neon on the facade from the π series.

Until 27 Jan Raoul Ubac – Photographies
Renn 14/16 Verneuil, 14-16 rue de Verneuil, 7th (01.42.61.25.71). Mº Rue du Bac. **Open** Tue-Sat noon-7pm. **Admission** free.
Photographic experimentation by the German who formed part of Surrealist circles in the 30s.

Until 28 Jan Thomas Demand
Fondation Cartier, 261 bd Raspail, 14th (01.42.18.56.50). **Open** Tue-Sun noon-8pm. **Admission** 3,81€
Pared-back photographs of architecture, interior details and objects mark a research into space and timelessness. Plus paintings by Bernard Piffaretti.

Until 4 Feb Raymond Depardon
Maison Européenne de la Photographie, 5-7 rue de Fourcy, 4th (01.44.78.75.00). Mº St-Paul. **Open** Wed-Sun 11am-8pm. **Admission** 4,57€
Retrospective of the Magnum photographer and documentary-maker from voyages through war-torn Lebanon to his latest book *Errance*.

Tue-Sun 11am-7pm. **Admission** 3,81€
The veteran of French nouveau realisme creates 20 works starting from 20 objects that each symbolise a century, developed in a dialogue with Umberto Eco.

12 Jan-25 Mar Mémoire des Camps
Hôtel de Sully, 62 rue St-Antoine, 4th (01.42.74.47.75). Mº Bastille or St-Paul. **Open** Tue-Sun 10am-6.30pm. **Admission** 3,81€
Taking an analytical approach, contemporary photographers are shown alongside period images of the Holocaust and the liberation of the camps.

24 Jan-9 Apr Alberto Giacometti: L'Oeuvre dessiné
Centre Pompidou (see above).
On the centenary of Giacometti's birth, a look at the graphic works that complement his sculptures.

26 Jan-24 Mar American Folk Art
Mona Bismarck Foundation, 34 av de New-York, 16th (01.47.23.38.88). Mº Alma-Marceau. **Open** Tue-Sat 10.30am-6.30pm. **Admission** free.
Folk art portraits painted by itinerant artists, carved shop signs from the Fenimore Art Museum.

22 Feb-20 May Rodin en 1900
Musée du Luxembourg, 19 rue de Vaugirard, 6th (01.42.34.25.95). Mº Odéon/RER Luxembourg. **Open** Tue-Sun 11am-6pm. **Admission** 4,73€

Au-delà du Spectacle

Au-delà du Spectacle

Until 11 Mar L'Ecole de Paris 1904-29
Musée d'Art Moderne de la Ville de Paris, 11 av du Président-Wilson, 16th (01.53.67.40.00). Mº Iéna or Alma-Marceau. **Open** Tue-Sun 10am-7pm. **Admission** 6,86€
Focusing on artistic Montmartre and Montparnasse, this exhibition questions the existence of a 'school' and points to the diverse heritages of Chagall, Modigliani, Foujita, Picasso, Man Ray or Kertesz.

15 Dec-31 Mar Vies de Chiens
Musée de la Chasse et de la Nature, 60 rue des Archives, 3rd (01.53.01.92.40). **Open** Tue-Sun 11am-6pm (Thur till 9pm). **Admission** 4,57€
A dog's life is clearly a happy one to judge from the pampered mutts in these oil paintings, and their bejewelled collars and paraphernalia.

20 Dec-21 Mar 20 Siècles vus par Arman
Couvent des Cordeliers, 15 rue de l'Ecole de Médecine, 6th (06.68.84.67.25). Mº Odéon. **Open**

A reconstitution of the 1900 Pavillon de l'Alma exhibition that consecrated the 60-year-old artist.

28 Feb-30 Apr Le Prix Marcel Duchamp
Centre Pompidou (see above).
Created by an association of French collectors, the Prix Duchamp hopes to be France's answer to the Turner Prize and bring visibility to the local scene. The winner announced on 1 Dec from the shortlist (Bismuth, Bournigault, Closky, Hirschhorn, Varini, Veilhan) gets 35,000€ and this prestigious show.

1 Mar-28 May Paul Signac
Grand Palais (see above). **Admission** 7,62€/8,54€
The first comprehensive exhibition of this major Post-Impressionist since 1963.

7 Mar-18 June Les Années Pop
Centre Pompidou (see above).
A pluri-disciplinary survey of Pop movements in art, film, architecture, design and music 1956-68.

Louvre

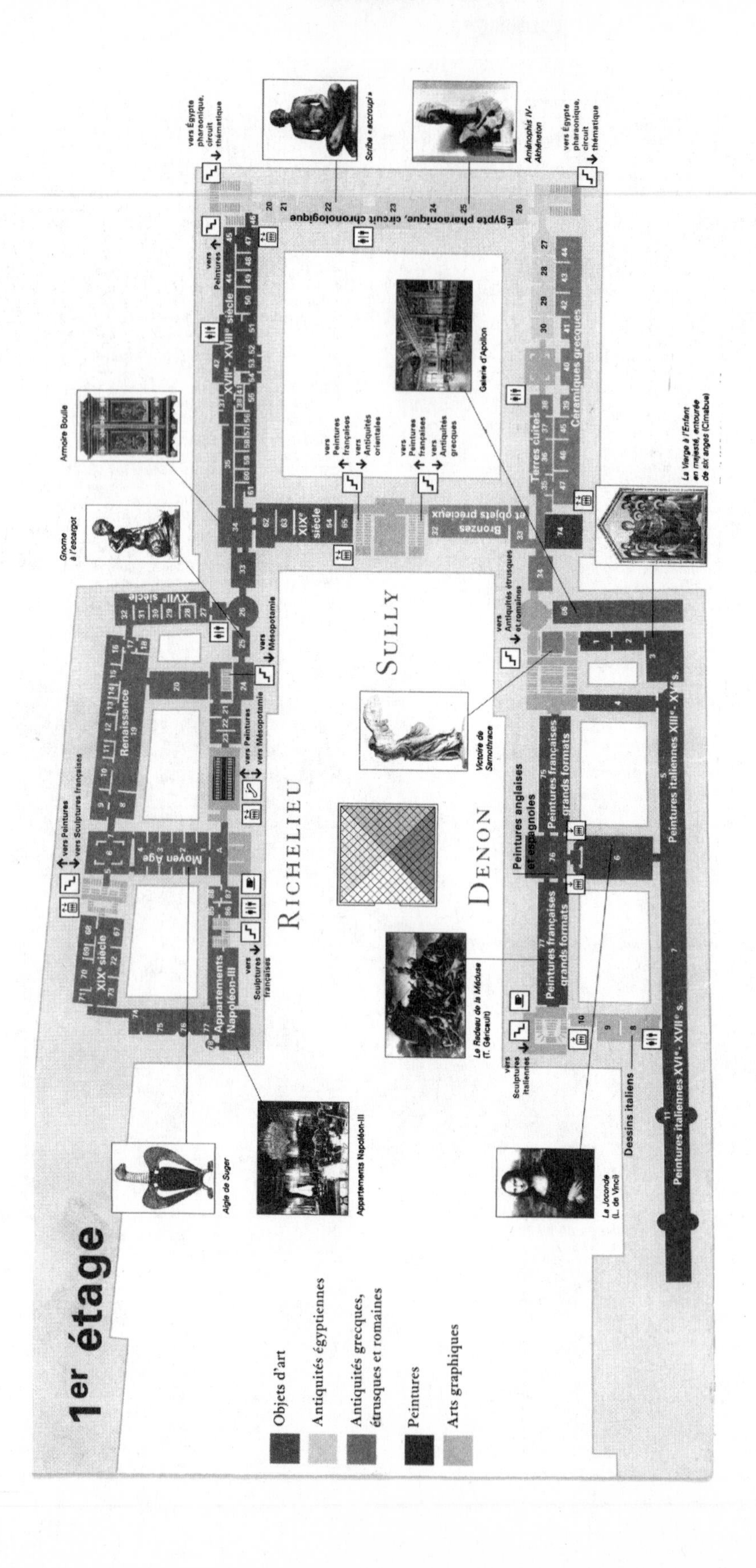
1er étage
Objets d'art
Antiquités égyptiennes
Antiquités grecques, étrusques et romaines
Peintures
Arts graphiques
Richelieu
Sully
Denon
Moyen Age
Renaissance
XVIIe siècle
XIXe siècle
Appartements Napoléon-III
XVIIe - XVIIIe siècle
Égypte pharaonique, circuit chronologique
Bronzes et objets précieux
Terres cuites
Céramiques grecques
Peintures françaises grands formats
Peintures anglaises et espagnoles
Peintures italiennes XIIIe - XVe s.
Peintures italiennes XVIe - XVIIe s.
Dessins italiens
Aigle de Suger
Appartements Napoléon-III
La Joconde (L. de Vinci)
Le Radeau de la Méduse (T. Géricault)
Victoire de Samothrace
Gnome à l'escargot
Armoire Boulle
Galerie d'Apollon
Scribe « accroupi »
Aménophis IV-Akhénaton
La Vierge à l'Enfant en majesté, entourée de six anges (Cimabue)

Animaux I

un cochon	un gorille	un lion	un taureau
un crocodile	un hippopotame	un mouton	un tigre
un éléphant	un kangourou	une panthère	une vache
une girafe	un léopard	un rhinocéros	

R.E.R.

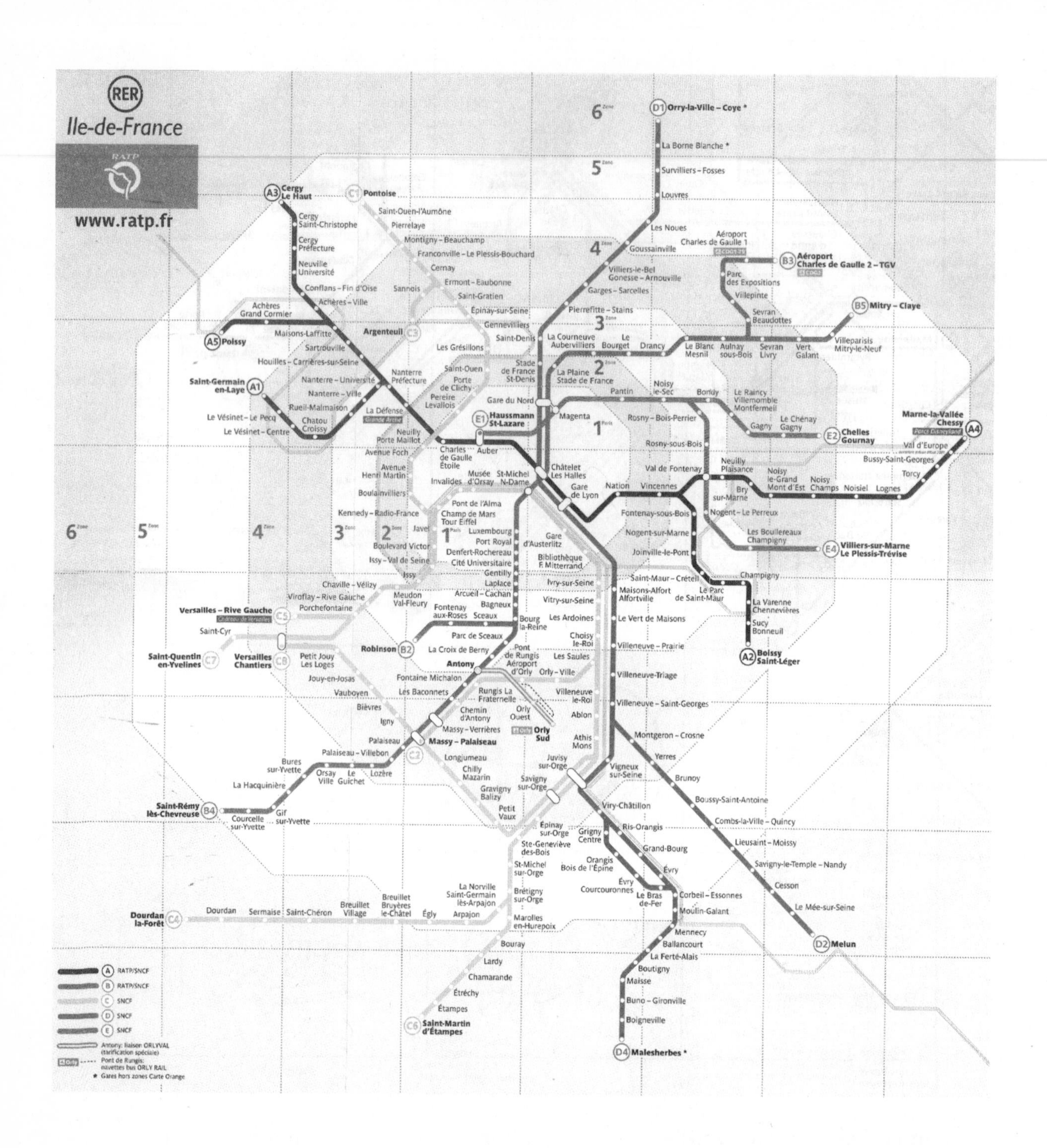
RER
Ile-de-France
RATP
www.ratp.fr
6 Zone
5 Zone
4 Zone
3 Zone
2 Zone
1 Paris
D1 Orry-la-Ville – Coye *
La Borne Blanche *
Survilliers – Fosses
Louvres
Les Noues
Goussainville
Aéroport Charles de Gaulle 1
Villiers-le-Bel Gonesse – Arnouville
Garges – Sarcelles
B3 Aéroport Charles de Gaulle 2 – TGV
Parc des Expositions
Villepinte
Sevran Beaudottes
B5 Mitry – Claye
Villeparisis Mitry-le-Neuf
A3 Cergy Le Haut
Cergy Saint-Christophe
Cergy Préfecture
Neuville Université
Conflans – Fin d'Oise
Achères – Ville
Achères Grand Cormier
A5 Poissy
Maisons-Laffitte
Sartrouville
Houilles – Carrières-sur-Seine
Saint-Germain en-Laye A1
Nanterre – Université
Nanterre – Ville
Rueil-Malmaison
Chatou Croissy
Le Vésinet – Le Pecq
Le Vésinet – Centre
C1 Pontoise
Saint-Ouen-l'Aumône
Pierrelaye
Montigny – Beauchamp
Franconville – Le Plessis-Bouchard
Cernay
Ermont – Eaubonne
Sannois
Saint-Gratien
Épinay-sur-Seine
Gennevilliers
Argenteuil C3
Les Grésillons
Saint-Denis
Pierrefitte – Stains
La Courneuve Aubervilliers
Le Bourget
Drancy
Le Blanc Mesnil
Aulnay sous-Bois
Sevran Livry
Vert Galant
Nanterre Préfecture
La Défense Grande Arche
Saint-Ouen
Porte de Clichy
Pereire Levallois
Stade de France St-Denis
La Plaine Stade de France
Pantin
Noisy le-Sec
Bondy
Le Raincy Villemomble Montfermeil
Gagny
Le Chénay Gagny
E2 Chelles Gournay
Marne-la-Vallée Chessy A4
Parcs Disneyland
Val d'Europe
Bussy-Saint-Georges
Torcy
Gare du Nord
Magenta
E1 Haussmann St-Lazare
Rosny – Bois-Perrier
Rosny-sous-Bois
Val de Fontenay
Neuilly Plaisance
Noisy le-Grand Mont d'Est
Noisy Champs
Noisiel
Lognes
Bry sur-Marne
Neuilly Porte Maillot
Avenue Foch
Charles de Gaulle Étoile
Auber
Avenue Henri Martin
Boulainvilliers
Invalides
Musée d'Orsay
St-Michel N-Dame
Châtelet Les Halles
Gare de Lyon
Nation
Vincennes
Fontenay-sous-Bois
Nogent – Le Perreux
Pont de l'Alma
Kennedy – Radio-France
Champ de Mars Tour Eiffel
Javel
Luxembourg
Port Royal
Denfert-Rochereau
Cité Universitaire
Boulevard Victor
Issy – Val de Seine
Issy
Gare d'Austerlitz
Bibliothèque F. Mitterrand
Nogent-sur-Marne
Joinville-le-Pont
Les Boullereaux Champigny
E4 Villiers-sur-Marne Le Plessis-Trévise
Champigny
Saint-Maur – Créteil
Maisons-Alfort Alfortville
Le Parc de Saint-Maur
La Varenne Chennevières
Sucy Bonneuil
A2 Boissy Saint-Léger
Chaville – Vélizy
Viroflay – Rive Gauche
Porchefontaine
Meudon Val-Fleury
Gentilly
Laplace
Arcueil – Cachan
Bagneux
Fontenay aux-Roses
Sceaux
Ivry-sur-Seine
Vitry-sur-Seine
Les Ardoines
Le Vert de Maisons
Versailles – Rive Gauche C5
Château de Versailles
Saint-Cyr
Saint-Quentin en-Yvelines C7
Versailles Chantiers C8
Petit Jouy Les Loges
Jouy-en-Josas
Vauboyen
Bièvres
Igny
Robinson B2
Parc de Sceaux
La Croix de Berny
Bourg la-Reine
Antony
Pont de Rungis Aéroport d'Orly
Choisy le-Roi
Les Saules
Orly – Ville
Villeneuve – Prairie
Villeneuve-Triage
Fontaine Michalon
Les Baconnets
Rungis La Fraternelle
Chemin d'Antony
Orly Ouest
Orly Sud
Villeneuve le-Roi
Ablon
Villeneuve – Saint-Georges
Massy – Verrières
Massy – Palaiseau
Palaiseau
Palaiseau – Villebon
C2
Longjumeau
Chilly Mazarin
Gravigny Balizy
Petit Vaux
Athis Mons
Juvisy sur-Orge
Savigny sur-Orge
Vigneux sur-Seine
Montgeron – Crosne
Yerres
Brunoy
Boussy-Saint-Antoine
Combs-la-Ville – Quincy
Lieusaint – Moissy
Savigny-le-Temple – Nandy
Cesson
Le Mée-sur-Seine
D2 Melun
Bures sur-Yvette
Orsay Ville
Le Guichet
Lozère
La Hacquinière
Saint-Rémy lès-Chevreuse B4
Courcelle sur-Yvette
Gif sur-Yvette
Viry-Châtillon
Ris-Orangis
Grand-Bourg
Évry
Grigny Centre
Orangis Bois de l'Épine
Évry Courcouronnes
Le Bras de-Fer
Corbeil – Essonnes
Moulin-Galant
Mennecy
Ballancourt
La Ferté-Alais
Boutigny
Maisse
Buno – Gironville
Boigneville
D4 Malesherbes *
Épinay sur-Orge
Ste-Geneviève des-Bois
St-Michel sur-Orge
Brétigny sur-Orge
Marolles en-Hurepoix
Bouray
Lardy
Chamarande
Étréchy
Étampes
C6 Saint-Martin d'Étampes
La Norville Saint-Germain lès-Arpajon
Arpajon
Égly
Breuillet Bruyères le-Châtel
Breuillet Village
Saint-Chéron
Sermaise
Dourdan
Dourdan la-Forêt C4
A RATP/SNCF
B RATP/SNCF
C SNCF
D SNCF
E SNCF
Antony: liaison ORLYVAL (tarification spéciale)
Pont de Rungis: navettes bus ORLY RAIL
* Gares hors zones Carte Orange

Disneyland Resort Paris

FESTIVAL HALLOWEEN PRATIQUE

Horaires d'ouverture: Le Festival Halloween aura lieu du 1er octobre au 4 novembre. Pendant cette période, le parc sera ouvert de **10 h à 20 h** du lundi au vendredi et de **9 h à 20 h** les samedis et dimanches et tous les jours à partir du 20 octobre.

Prix du passeport d'entrée 1 jour au Parc Disneyland: valable du 1er octobre au 4 novembre

Adulte	35,98€
Enfant 3 à 11 ans inclus	28,05€

Un exemple de forfait:

Le forfait "Bella Notte" 1 nuit/2 jours: une formule simple et pratique. Il comprend une nuit d'hôtel, le petit déjeuner et deux journées dans le Parc Disneyland. On peut également y inclure le transport en TGV SNCF ou en avion Air France.

Exemple de forfait "Bella Notte" sans transport:
À partir de **106,56€*** par adulte (base 2 adultes) et **52,59€** par enfant de 3 à 11 ans inclus.

* Prix valables pour les arrivées du dimanche au jeudi inclus, du 01/10 au 02/11, selon disponibilité. Tarif calculé par adulte (sur la base de 2 adultes) et par enfant (3 à 11 ans inclus) partageant la même chambre à l'hôtel Sante Fe.

Où se procurer les passeports d'entrée:
- ➪ par téléphone au 01 60 30 60 30 (7 jours sur 7)
- ➪ aux guichets à l'entrée du parc
- ➪ par minitel 3615 Disneyland (0,34€/mn)
- ➪ dans les boutiques Disney Store de Paris et de province
- ➪ dans les billeteries Auchan, Carrefour, FNAC, Virgin Megastore et France Billet de Paris et de province
- ➪ à l'Office du Tourisme de Paris et dans les aéroports parisiens
- ➪ dans les principaux guichets RATP à Paris (métro et RER)

Plan de Bordeaux

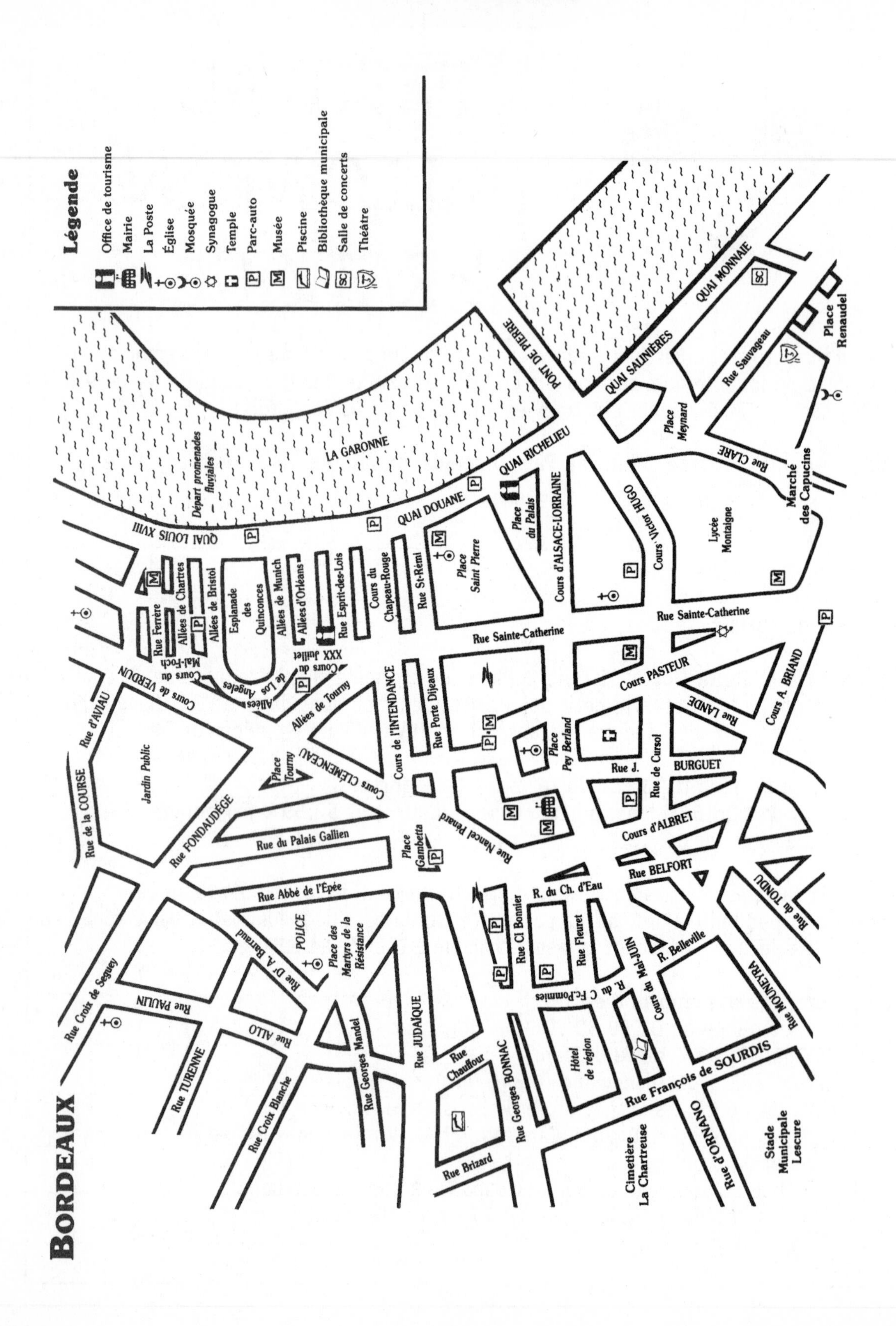

Mots croisés

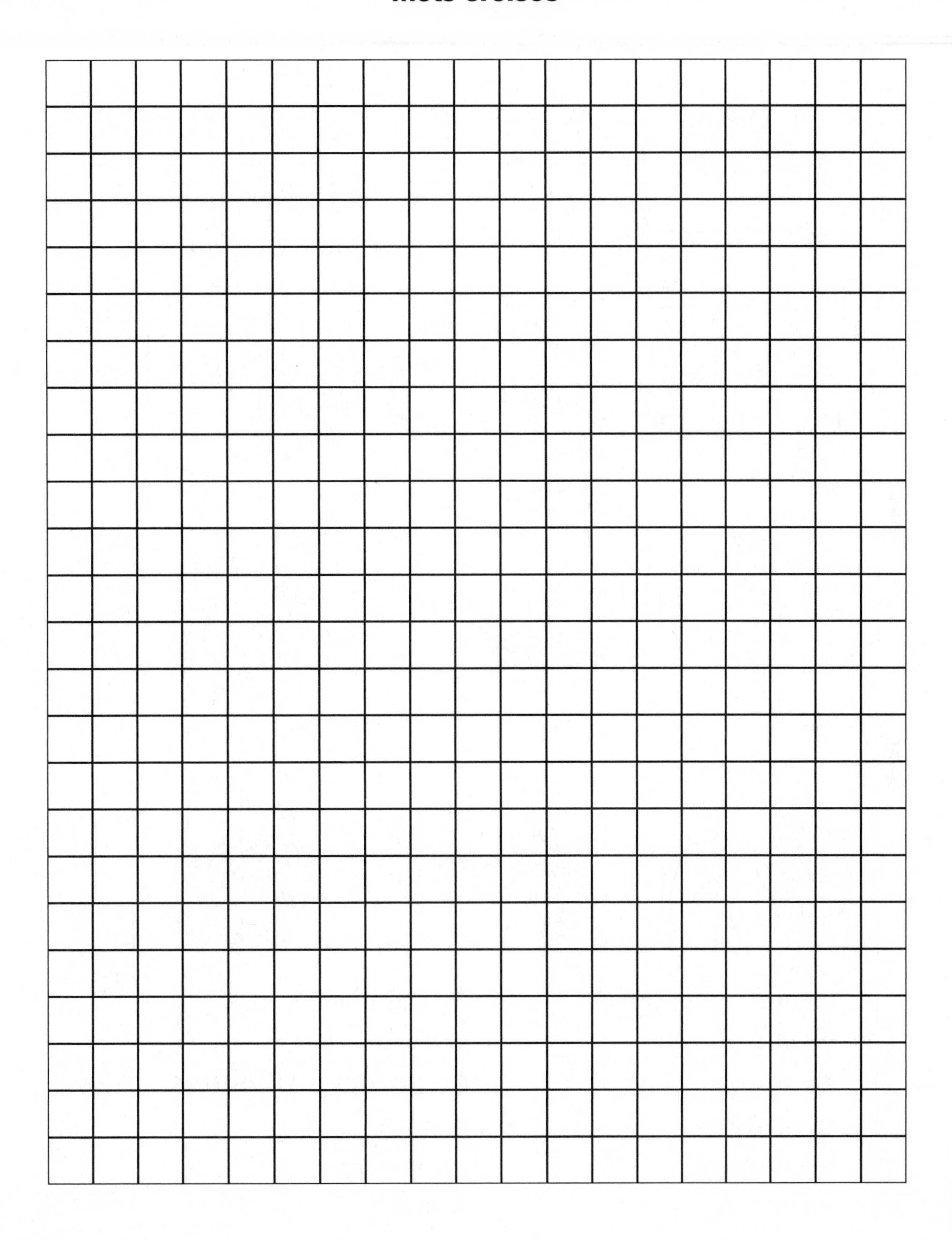

Moyens de transport

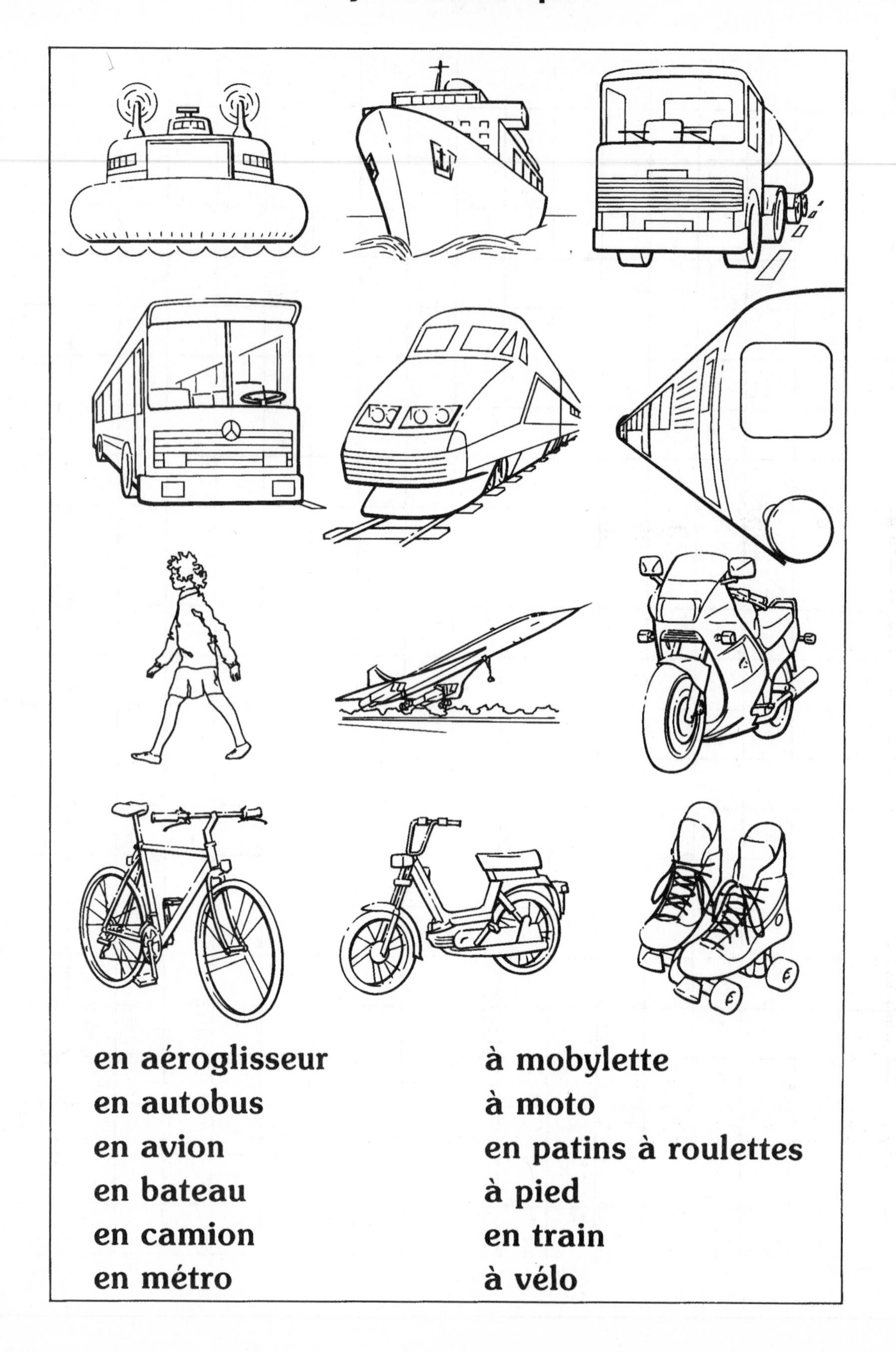

Horaire des trains I

Paris - Bruxelles - Amsterdam

Nº du Thalys		9305 (1)	9307 (2)	9309	9413 (3)	9317
Paris-Nord	dép.	**06:34**	**06:55**	**07:37**	**08:37**	**09:37**
Mons	arr.					**11:02**
Bruxelles-Midi	arr.	**08:40**	**09:02**	**09:40**	**10:40**	**11:42**
Bruxelles-Midi	dép.	08:56	09:10	**09:45**	10:56 (4)	11:56 (4)
Antwerpen-Centraal (Anvers)	arr.	09:42	09:49		11:42 (4)	12:42 (4)
Berchem (Anvers)	arr.			**10:25**		
Rotterdam CS	arr.			**11:27**		
Den Haag HS (La Haye)	arr.			**11:44**		
Schiphol-Aéroport	arr.			**12:10**		
Amsterdam CS	arr.			**12:28**		

		9305	9307	9309	9413	9317
circule	Lundi à vendredi	circule	circule	circule	circule	circule
ne circule pas	Samedi	ne circule pas	ne circule pas	circule	circule	circule
	Dimanche	ne circule pas	ne circule pas	circule	circule	circule

(1) Ne circule pas du 13 juillet au 1er septembre

(2) Ne circule pas le 15 août

(3) Ne circule pas les dimanches du 2 au 28 juin et du 2 au 28 septembre

(4) Ne circule pas les samedis et dimanches ni le 15 août

(5) Ne circule pas les samedis et dimanches du 2 au 28 juin et du 2 au 28 septembre

Marseille

SITES À DÉCOUVRIR

Le Vieux Port ❷

Le Lacydon des Grecs, actuellement port de plaisance parfaitement abrité fût un motif idéal pour ***Verdilhan***, ***Marquet*** ou ***Signac***. Le voir depuis le bas des Jardins du Pharo au soleil couchant, ou longer à pied la promenade Louis Brauquier au pied du Fort Saint Jean.

La Corniche ❸

Après le Parc du Pharo, l'avenue J.F Kennedy, ancienne Corniche, longe la côte sur 3 km. D'un bout à l'autre, elle offre de superbes points de vue, que l'on retrouve dans les œuvres de ***Jean-Baptiste Olive*** et ***Edouard Crémieux***. De la Corniche, on peut voir les îles et la rade de Marseille.

Les Goudes ❹

Le peintre ***Adolphe Moutte*** nous entraîne hors des sentiers battus, au bout de la promenade du bord de mer. Lieu insolite, ce petit port de pêche a conservé son côté pittoresque. En poursuivant la route du Cap Croisette, on traverse un paysage du bout du monde, à la découverte de l'île Maine.

❷ **Henri Manguin**
"Fenêtre sur le Vieux-Port de Marseille", 1925 - ***Musée Ziem, Martigues***

❷ **Albert Marquet** - "Le port de Marseille" vers 1915 - ***Musée Cantini, Marseille***

❹ **Adolphe Moutte** - "Les Goudes", 1910
F.R.A.O.P, Marseille.

À LA RENCONTRE DES PEINTRES

- **Le Musée Cantini ❺**
19, rue Grignan. Métro : Estrangin-Préfecture. Ouvert de 10h. à 17h. t.l.j. sauf lundi et jours feriés.
Tarif : 2,29€ T.R : 1,14€ Gratuit le dim. mat. Visite commentée français et anglais sur demande.
Tél : 04.91.54.77.75
Y sont exposées des œuvres de Marquet, Seyssaud, Lombard, Dufy, Camoin, Derain, Matisse, Picasso, Chagall.

- **Le Musée des Beaux-Arts ❻**
Palais Longchamp.
Métro : Cinq Avenues-Longchamp.
Début oct. à fin mai : ouvert de 10h à 17h. Début juin à fin septembre de 11h à 18h, t.l.j. sauf lundi et jours fériés. Entrée gratuite dim. mat.
Tarif: 1,83€ T.R:0,91€
Tél : 04.91.14.59.30. La galerie du XIX° siècle présente l'école des paysagistes provençaux, vous y trouverez des œuvres de Monticelli, Guigou, Olive...

- **Le Musée Grobet-Labadié ❼**
140, bd Longchamp.
Métro : Cinq Avenues - Longchamp.
Tél : 04.91.62.21.82.
Ouvert de 10h. à 17h., sauf lundi et jours feriés. Visite commentée tous les sam. et dim. à 15h.
Le marchand marseillais Alexandre Labadié fit construire cette demeure en 1873. Riche de quelques 5000 objets d'art, le musée possède des paysages de Guigou, Monticelli, Loubon, Ziem...

OFFICE DE TOURISME ❶
4, la Canebière
Tél : 04.91.13.89.00
Fax : 04.91.13.89.20
Web : http : //www.mairie-marseille.fr

❸ **Edouard Crémieux** - "La corniche à Marseille"
Musée de la Castre, Cannes

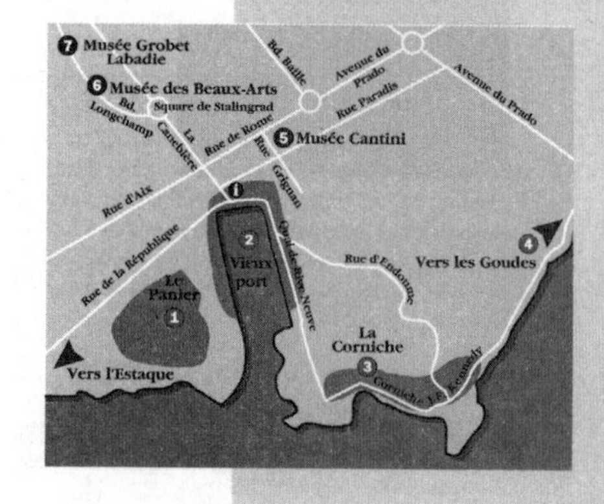

9

Œuvre de Cézanne

Différentes étapes de l'œuvre de Cézanne

PERIODE ROMANTIQUE 1859-1871

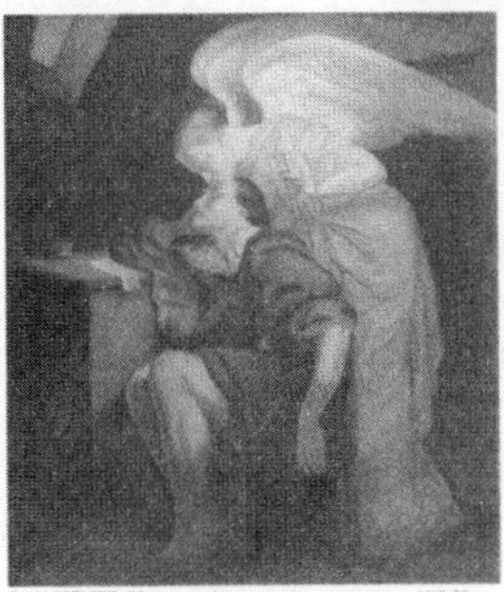

Le baiser de la Muse
Dépôt Musée Granet* - Aix

Nature morte : Sucrier, poires et tasse bleue
Dépôt Musée Granet* - Aix

PERIODE IMPRESSIONNISTE 1872-1877

La maison du Docteur Gachet
Musée d'Orsay - Paris

Bethsabée
Dépôt Musée Granet* - Aix

PERIODE CONSTRUCTIVE 1878-1887

Vase bleu
Musée d'Orsay - Paris

Portrait de Madame Cézanne
Dépôt Musée Granet* - Aix

PERIODE SYNTHETIQUE 1886-1906

La montagne Sainte Victoire
"Cabinet dessins" du Louvre

Baigneuses
Dépôt Musée Granet* - Aix

Messages

MESSAGE

Message pour: ....

Jour: .... **Heure:** ....

.... **a téléphoné.**

Message ....

....

....

....

....

MESSAGE

Message pour: ....

Jour: .... **Heure:** ....

.... **a téléphoné.**

Message ....

....

....

....

....

MESSAGE

Message pour: ....

Jour: .... **Heure:** ....

.... **a téléphoné.**

Message ....

....

....

....

....

MESSAGE

Message pour: ....

Jour: .... **Heure:** ....

.... **a téléphoné.**

Message ....

....

....

....

....

Animaux II

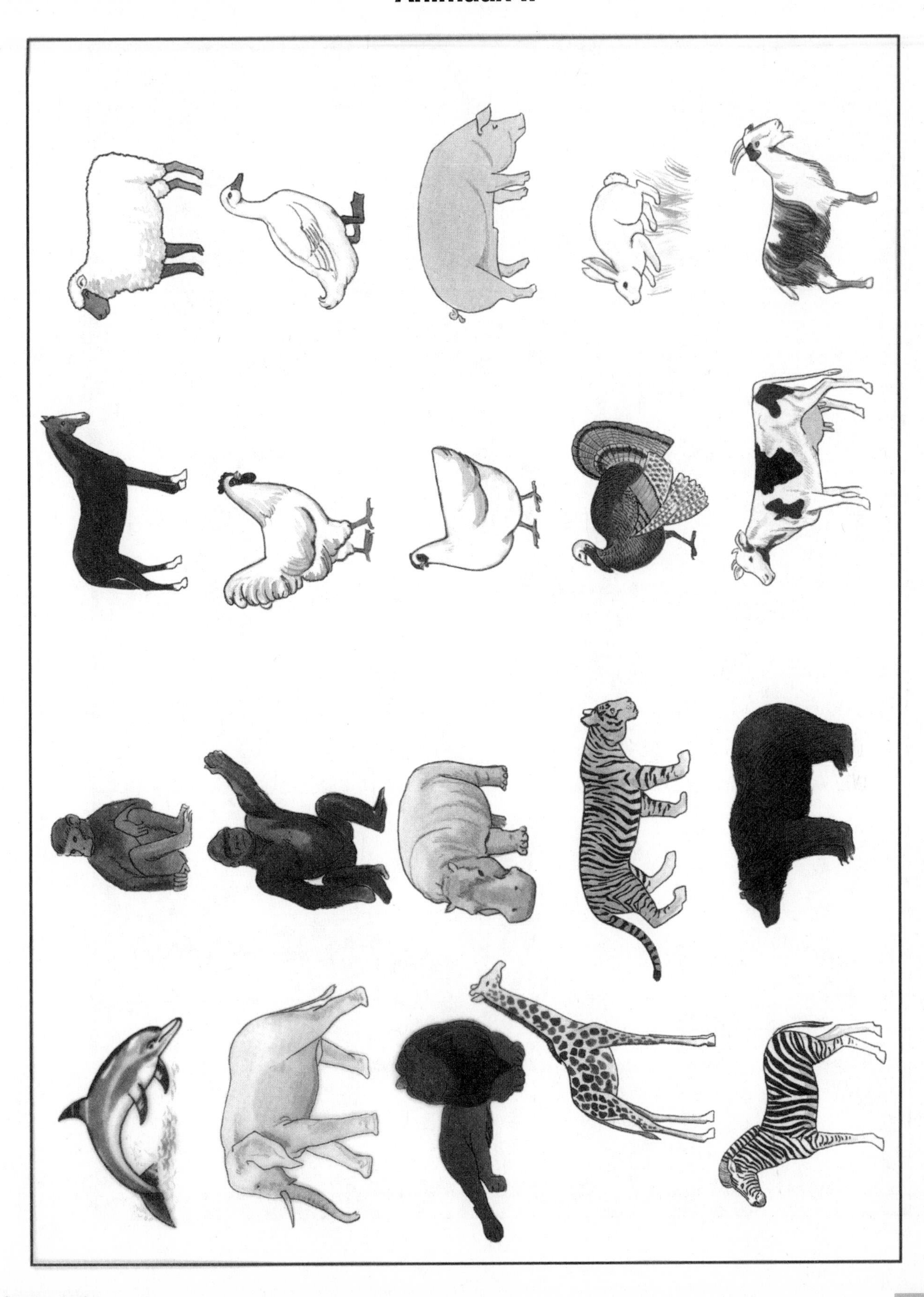

La ferme et ses animaux

Qu'est-ce qu'ils lisent?

Provinces et produits de France

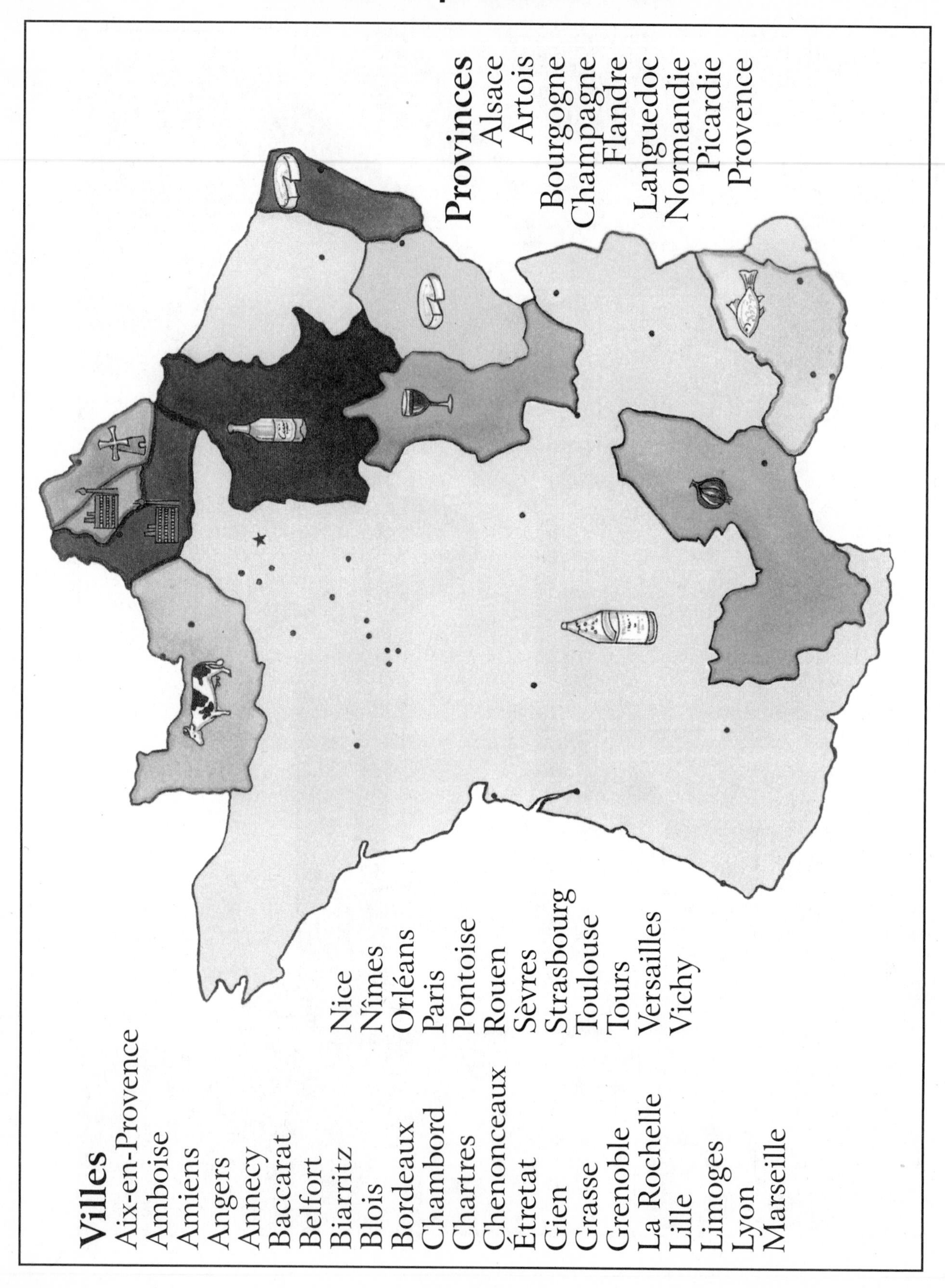

Au restaurant I

Au restaurant II

Chez Jean-Paul

Menu

Suggestions du jour

Consommé au vermicelle

Soupe de poisson

Hors-d'œuvre

Assiette de crudités
Pâté du chef
Sardines beurre
Pamplemousse au naturel

Assiette de charcuterie
Thon mayonnaise
Moules marinière

Viandes et poissons

Escalope de veau à la crème
Canard à l'orange
Entrecôte bordelaise
Côtelette de porc
Truite aux amandes

Tripes à la mode de Caen
Poulet au riz
Coq au vin
Sole meunière

Omelettes au choix (champignons, espagnole, fines herbes, jambon, nature)

Légumes

Pommes duchesse
Petits pois
Salade verte

Pommes frites
Haricots verts au beurre

Fromages

Brie
Chèvre

Gruyère
Camembert

Emmenthal
Port-Salut

Desserts

Crème au caramel
Glace maison
Crêpes bretonnes

Baba au rhum
Tarte aux pommes

Boissons

Vin rouge du pays
Beaujolais Villages
Mâcon
Coca
Café

Vin blanc du pays
Côtes du Rhône
Bière
Eau minérale

Service et taxes en supplément - 15%

Menu à prix fixe - 22€

Soupe à l'oignon
Melon
Artichaut vinaigrette
Salade de tomates

Poulet rôti garni
Escalope de veau
Steak frites
Omelette aux fines herbes

Fromage
Tarte aux fraises
Glace
Fruits

Service compris

Menu

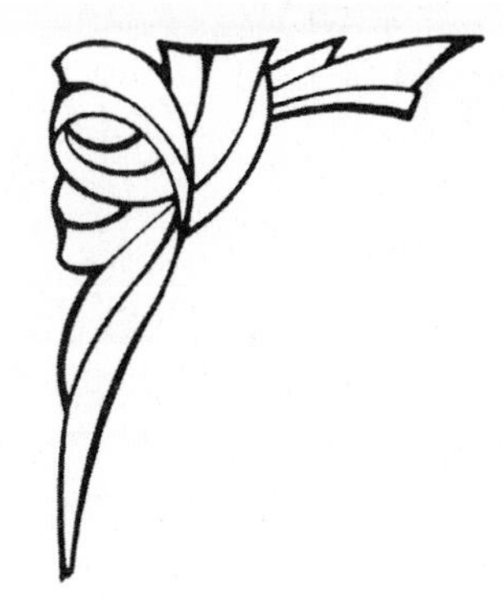

Hors-d'œuvre

Entrées

Poissons et Viandes

Légumes

Desserts

Boissons

Addition

RESTAURANT
La Coquille

8, rue de l'Arche

37550 Saint-Avertin

Table no .... Le ....

Merci de votre visite À bientôt	Montant		
	Service %		
	Total à payer		

Léon de Bruxelles

Grande Salade "Princesse Charlotte"

9,50€

Saumon fumé, noix, salade, toast, oignons, citron, vinaigrette

11,97€

Moules au roquefort

roquefort, vin blanc, crème, pommes frites

La coupe Léon

glace vanille, salade de fruits frais, sauce fraise, chantilly

Mousse au chocolat

Pour 4 personnes
Préparation: 25 mn

Les ingrédients:
5 œufs, blancs séparés des jaunes
150 g de sucre
300 g de chocolat à croquer
1 cuillerée à soupe d'eau
75 g de beurre ramolli
1 pincée de sel

Ustensiles:
2 jattes
1 bol
1 fouet
1 petite casserole
1 cuillère en bois

- Battre au fouet dans une jatte les jaunes d'œufs et le sucre pour obtenir un mélange blanc et crémeux: on dit qu'il fait le ruban.
- Faire fondre le chocolat et l'eau dans une petite casserole à feu très doux, sans le faire cuire, pour obtenir une pâte lisse. S'il a commencé à cuire, ne vous désespérez pas: ajoutez plutôt, hors du feu, une goutte d'eau en remuant.
- En tournant rapidement, verser le chocolat sur les jaunes. Ajouter le beurre en remuant pour qu'il fonde.
- Mettre une pincée de sel dans les blancs d'œufs et les monter en neige très ferme.
- Incorporer les blancs délicatement au mélange œufs-chocolat.
- Laisser reposer une journée ou une nuit au réfrigérateur.

Suggestion:
Présenter la mousse au chocolat dans une soupière ou un saladier blanc, ou dans de petits pots individuels. Ajouter, si l'on veut, une rosette de crème fouettée.

Coq au vin

Ingrédients pour 6 personnes:

1 coq de 1,5 kg à 2 kg
150 g de beurre
300 g de morilles fraîches
50 g de farine
30 cl de vin rouge
75 cl de crème fraîche
sel, poivre

Préparation:

1. Découper le coq en morceaux et frotter ceux-ci de sel, de poivre et de farine.
2. Les faire revenir de tous les côtés sans colorer, couvrir et mettre à four moyen 20 minutes.
3. Retirer du four, mettre les morceaux de côté, dégraisser, déglacer et ajouter le vin rouge.
4. Retourner les morceaux, ajouter les morilles bien nettoyées et la crème.
5. Laisser sur feu doux sans couvrir et rectifier l'assaisonnement si nécessaire, jusqu'à ce que la sauce réduite soit brillante (minimum 30 minutes).

La gastronomie est un art de vivre très français. Et c'est à Lyon qu'elle prend toute sa saveur. Cette ville où grandes tables et petits bouchons font les délices des gourmands.

ART DE VIVRE GOURMET

On les appelait "les mères". Ces femmes à la forte personnalité et au tour de main remarquable ont formé au début du siècle des générations de chefs lyonnais qui ont façonné la réputation gastronomique de la ville.

Aujourd'hui l'art du "bien manger" se célèbre dans le cadre magnifique des grandes tables référencées par les guides spécialisés, toutes étapes indispensables et nombreuses à Lyon. Il peut aussi se déguster dans l'ambiance plus simple d'un bouchon. On s'y régale des spécialités lyonnaises, celles qui font partie d'un patrimoine populaire cher à tout vrai Lyonnais : le saucisson de Lyon, le Jésus, le cervelas truffé, la quenelle, les gratons, le tablier de sapeur ou la salade de clapotons. On y apprécie surtout une ambiance naturelle et bon enfant qui réconforte.

Pour sentir ces liens qui unissent Lyon à la bonne chère, il faut respirer l'atmosphère des grands marchés lyonnais : celui du quai Saint-Antoine en bord de Saône, face au panorama éblouissant de la colline de Fourvière, ou celui de la Croix-Rousse dans les hauteurs, un des quartiers les plus vivants de la ville. Tous deux bénéficient d'une animation sympathique où grands chefs et ménagères se croisent.

Dans le troisième arrondissement, les Halles montrent aussi cette ambiance gourmande et chaleureuse. Le spécialiste du fromage, celui du poisson, celui de la charcuterie, interpellent le passant et chacun discute familièrement avec ses clients.

LA GRANDE CUISINE

Lyon est la ville de France qui possède le plus grand nombre d'étoiles au Guide Michelin (hors Paris) et de grands chefs célèbres.

LES BOUCHONS

Petits restaurants servant dans un décor pittoresque des spécialités à base de cochonaille, arrosée de pots de Beaujolais ou de Côtes-du-Rhône. Au menu : gratons, salade lyonnaise, tablier de sapeur, andouillette, gras-double, paillasson, cervelle de canut, etc...

LES HALLES - LES MARCHÉS - LES TRAITEURS

Pour mieux apprécier la cuisine lyonnaise, il faut aller flâner sur les marchés du Quai Saint-Antoine (2e) et du Boulevard de la Croix-Rousse (4e), cotoyer les habitués des Halles, 102 cours Lafayette (3e), ou dans le centre ville pour déguster ou acheter des spécialités (quenelles, saucisson brioché, cervelas truffé, fromages).

Demandez le "Guide de Lyon" (liste hôtels, restaurants, nocturne, shopping) à l'Office du Tourisme de Lyon.

Consultez le 3615 Lyon 0,34€ la min.

Contactez un musée d'art à Paris

Imagine you are going to Paris. You would like to visit one of the Paris art museums you learned about in **Unité 2.** Using what you know about writing a formal letter in French from the **Lecture** section, write a letter requesting a map and a brochure from the museum you would like to visit. You might also inquire about any special exhibits that will be held during the time of your stay in Paris.

Begin your letter by saying when you are going to visit Paris. Then make your request using polite, courteous French. Remember to use **vous** instead of **tu**. Finally, use a formal closing. Below are some expressions that will help you and a list of addresses that you can choose from.

- *pourriez-vous*: would you be able to
- *un plan*: map
- *une brochure*: brochure
- *spécial(e)*: special

le Louvre
99, rue de Rivoli

le musée d'Orsay
1, rue de la Légion d'honneur

le musée Marmottan
2, rue Louis-Boilly

le musée national d'art moderne au Centre Pompidou
place Georges Pompidou

le musée Picasso
Hôtel Salé
5, rue de Thorigny

Affaires de toilette

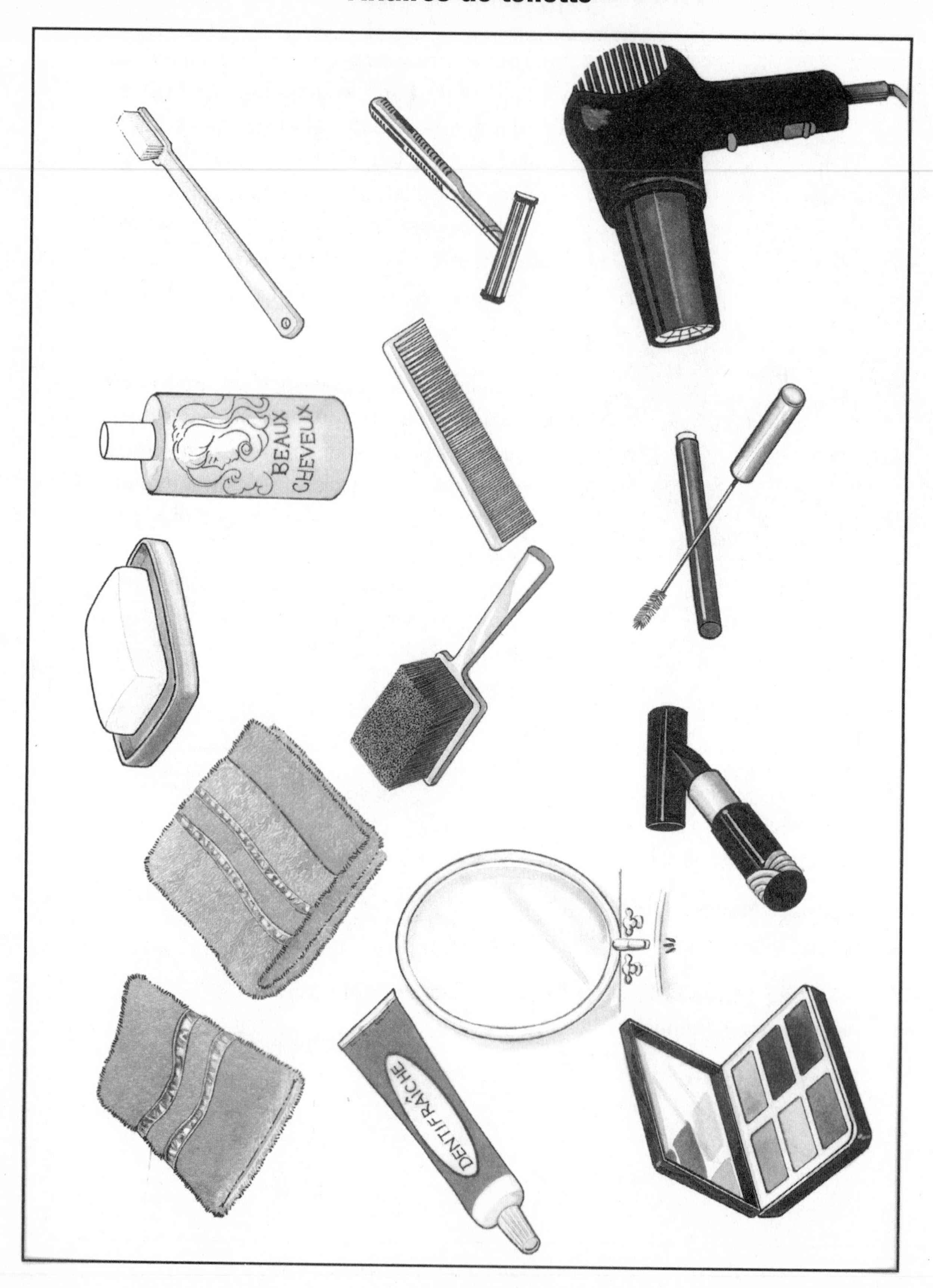

La journée de Claire

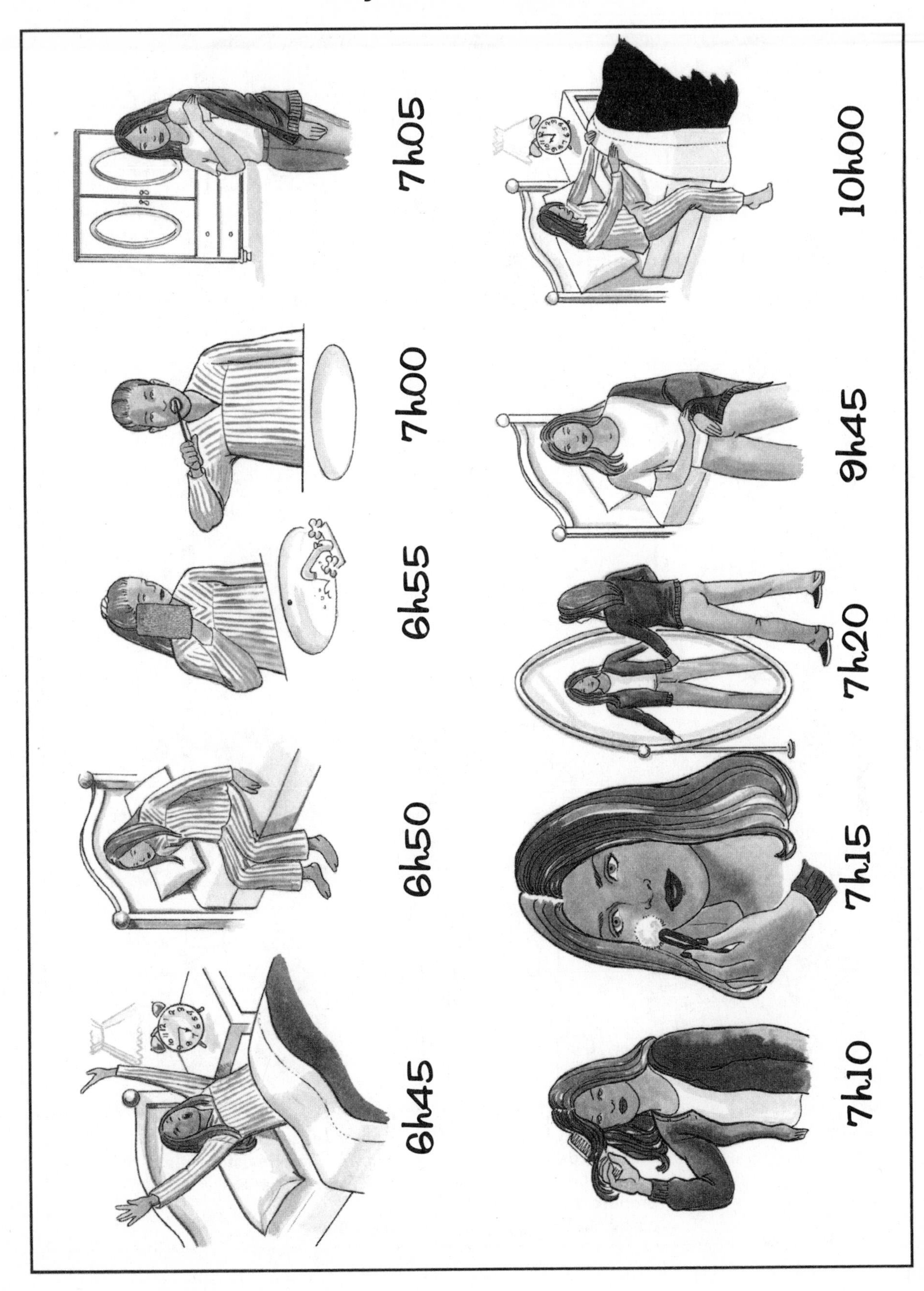

La journée d'Yves

se brosser les dents
se coucher
s'habiller
se laver
se lever
se réveiller

arriver au collège
écouter la radio
faire ses devoirs
prendre le petit déjeuner
prendre une douche
quitter la maison

quitter le collège
ranger ses affaires
regarder la télévision/télé
revenir à la maison
sortir
travailler

Appareils électroménagers

BIEN CHOISIR

LA REDOUTE vous propose une gamme complète d'aspirateurs. Testés pour vous dans nos laboratoires, ils vous garantissent les plus hautes performances et les meilleurs rapports qualité/prix.
L'efficacité d'un aspirateur se mesure par sa puissance, sa dépression (pouvoir de succion) mesurée en millimètres, son débit (vitesse de circulation de l'air entraînant les poussières) mesuré en litres d'air par seconde.

G 3 versions pour cet aspirateur M'TEC **compact**, léger et très maniable. Qualité Valeur Sûre. Equipé d'un filtre moteur et d'un filtre purificateur d'air. Sortie flexible pivotant à 360° pour un maximum de maniabilité. Accroche-tube au dos de l'appareil pour pouvoir le ranger facilement. Témoin de remplissage du sac (sauf modèle 1200 W), capacité 6 l. Tube métal chromé. Enrouleur de câble automatique. Livré avec 1 brosse pour tapis et sol dur, tuyère fine et suceur meubles. Dimensions 46 x 27 x 20 cm. Poids 5 kg env. Coloris anthracite. Garantie 1 an. S.A.V. assuré, voir p. 1220.

- **Modèle 1200 W automatique.** Débit d'air 48 l/s. Dépression 2000 mm. Consommation 320 Wh. 642.4228 **85,22€**
- **Modèle 1300 W, avec variateur électronique** de puissance. Dépression 2200 mm. Débit d'air 50 l/s. Consommation 370 Wh. Réf. 642.4236 **100€**
- **Modèle 1400 W, avec variateur électronique** de puissance. Dépression 2400 mm. Débit d'air 53 l/s. Consommation 420 Wh. Réf. 642.4511 **115 €**

Lot de 10 sacs papier pour G. Réf. 441.4136 **12,04€**

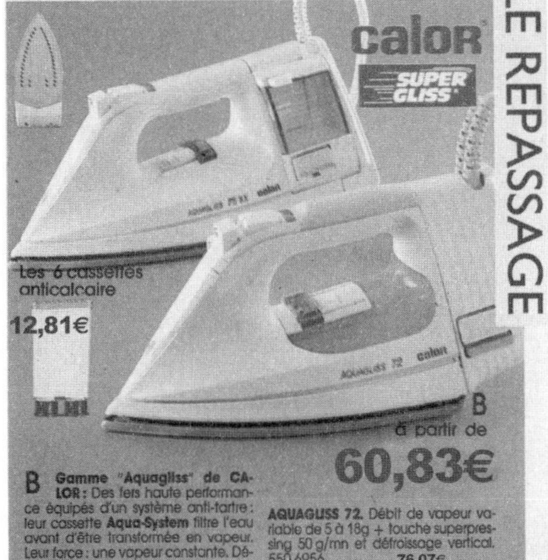

B à partir de **60,83€**

B Gamme "Aquagliss" de CALOR : Des fers haute performance équipés d'un système anti-tartre : leur cassette **Aqua-System** filtre l'eau avant d'être transformée en vapeur. Leur force : une vapeur constante. Débit puissant. Touche pressing pour tissus difficiles et faux-plis rebelles. Record de vitesse : la **forme exclusive** de la semelle SUPERGLISS ACTIF en **DURILIUM II** inaltérable permet de repasser à double sens. Pulvérisateur. Cordon orientable avec enrouleur. Puissance 1200 W. 220 V. Poids 1,4 kg. Garantie 1 an voir p. 1220. **4 modèles :**

AQUAGLISS 60 S : modèle à débit de vapeur constant de 18 g + touche pressing 35g/mn. 549.4940 **prix 60,83€**

AQUAGLISS 72. Débit de vapeur variable de 5 à 18g + touche superpressing 50 g/mn et défroissage vertical. 550.6956 **76,07€**

AQUAGLISS 82 electronic. Modèle identique au précédent + système électronique de sécurité : arrêt automatique après 30 sec. à plat ou 8 mn sur le talon. Réf. 547.0943 **88,27€**

AQUAGLISS 75 S. Débit variable de 5 à 18 g + touche superpressing 50 g/mn. Réservoir transparent amovible, à remplir directement sous le robinet. Réf. 550.7030 **91,32€**

- Le lot de 6 cassettes AQUAGLISS anti-calcaire double durée. 547.0951 **Le lot 12,81€**

▲ SEMELLE SUPERGLISS CASSETTE ANTI-TARTRE

LA CARTE KANGOUROU
A crédit à partir de 30,49€ par mois. Voir p. 638

modèle luxe

VALEUR SÛRE

modèle économique

C'EST la fête !
C À PARTIR DE
266,79€
PRIX EN BAISSE

C Le mini lave-vaisselle. Qualité Valeur Sûre. Ultra-compact, il s'installe très facilement sur un évier, un plan de travail et peut même s'encastrer. Idéal pour un studio ou une caravane. Il se raccorde au robinet d'eau chaude ou froide. Vidange dans l'évier ou raccord sur syphon. Garantie 2 ans, voir p. 1220. 2 modèles :

Modèle économique. Capacité 14 assiettes + 10 verres + couverts. Cons. 13,5 l. 0,8 Kwh. Durée du cycle de lavage 20 mn (alimentation eau chaude 55°) ou 35 mn (alimentation eau froide). Distributeur automatique du liquide de rinçage. Programme automatique 55°. Sécurité anti-débordement, détecteurs de surchauffe et arrêt en cas d'ouverture de la porte. Cuve et paroi Inox. Porte anti-choc. Puissance 1170 W. 220V. dim. (HxLxP) 46 x 43 x 49,5 cm. 328.3003 **266,79€**

Modèle luxe. Capacité supérieure 16 assiettes + 8 verres + 4 tasses + couverts. Mêmes caractéristiques que ci-dessus avec système anti-calcaire permanent (plus besoin de sel), ouverture automatique de la porte en fin de cycle, double paroi pour une meilleure isolation phonique. 2 températures : 50° et 65°. Cuve Inox, parois extérieures acier galvanisé laqué blanc. Puissance 1230 W. Dim. (HxLxP) 47 x 43,5 x 51 cm. Poids 19 kg. 328.2856 **327,77€**

On fait le ménage chez les Dupont.

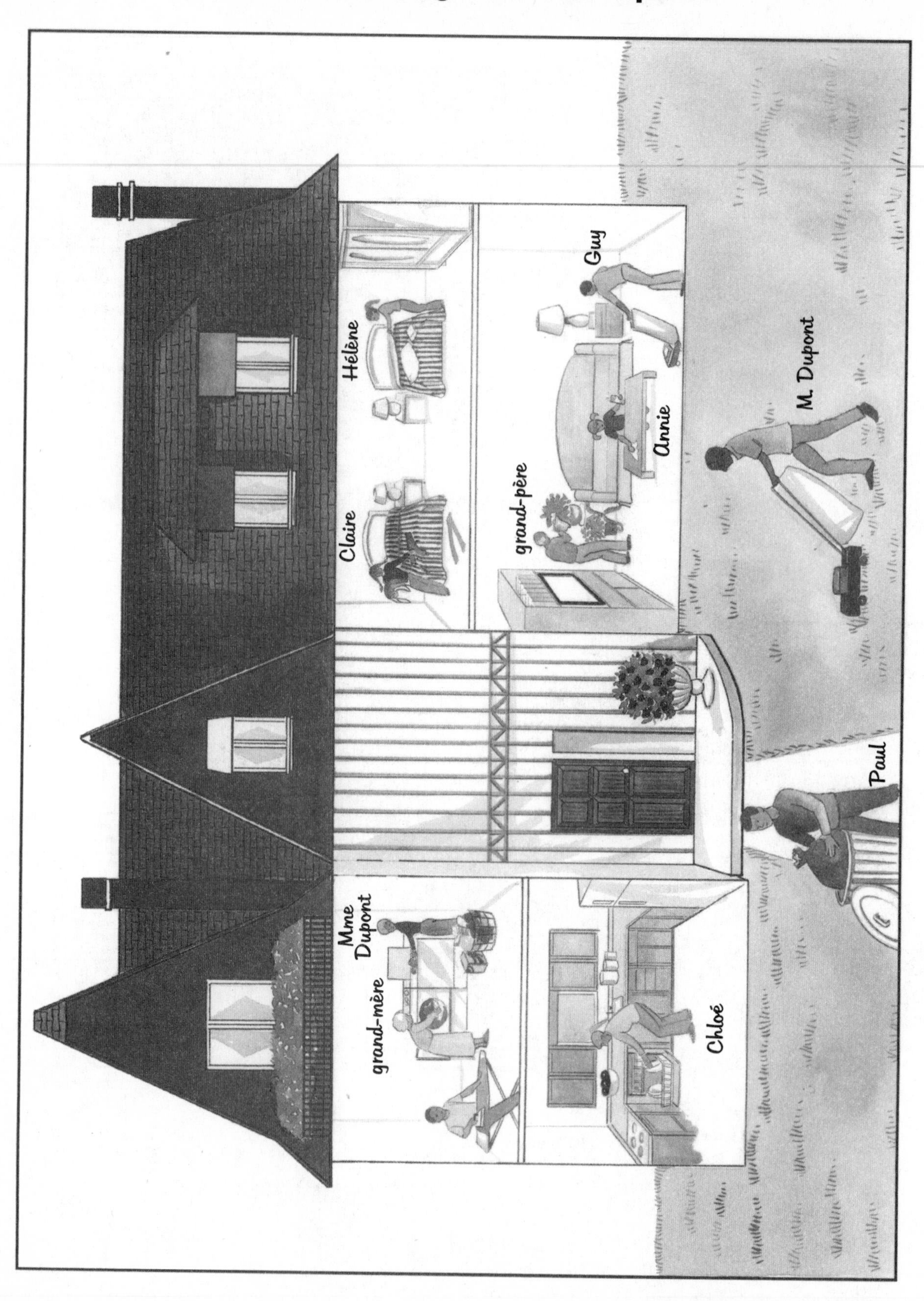

Corvées

balayer	**faire la lessive**	**nettoyer**
bricoler	**faire le lit**	**passer l'aspirateur**
faire les courses	**faire la vaisselle**	**repasser**
faire la cuisine	**mettre la table**	**travailler dans le jardin**

Pays francophones

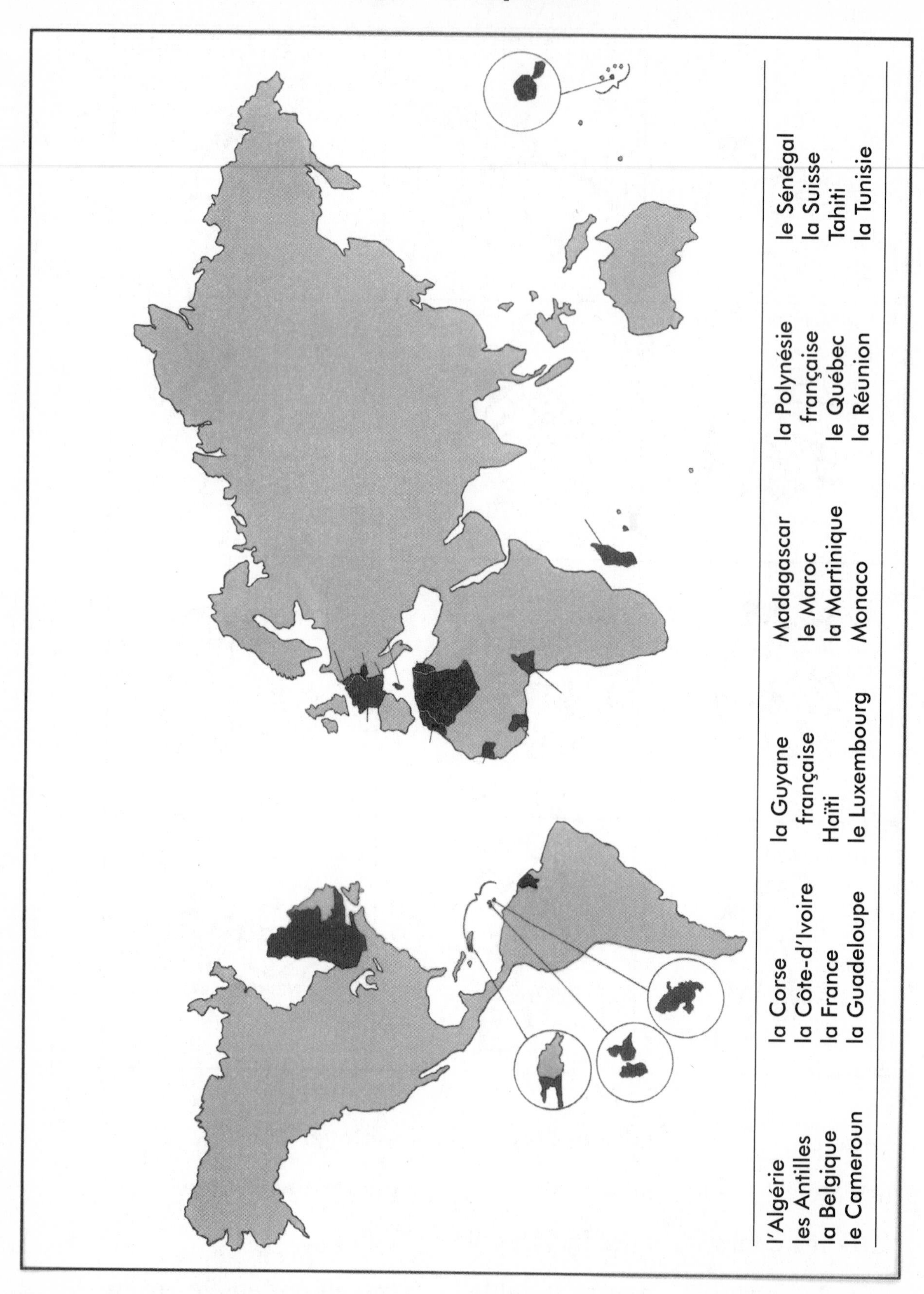

Haïti

Imaginez que vous travaillez pour HaïtiTourisme. Des gens qui veulent voyager en Haïti vous envoient des e-mails avec leurs questions. Écrivez-leur (*write them*) avec des renseignements (*information*) de votre site Internet. (Tapez "Haïti la Secrétairerie d'État au Tourisme" en vous servant de votre outil de recherche préféré.)

Nom: Amandine
Pays: Canada
Bonjour! Je vais voyager en Haïti au mois de février. Je voudrais louer une voiture. Pourriez-vous me donner une liste des agences de location de voitures? Où est-ce que je peux trouver un chauffeur-guide? Merci d'avance!

Nom: Tiffany
Pays: États-Unis
Je fais des recherches pour une dissertation que je dois écrire sur Haïti à l'école. Pourriez-vous m'aider? Quelles sont les religions principales d'Haïti? Quelle est la monnaie officielle? Quelles sont les langues officielles? Je vous remercie.

Nom: Xavier
Pays: France
Je vais passer une semaine à Cap Haïtien pour le travail. Quel est l'aéroport le plus proche?

Nom: Marie-Alix
Pays: Guadeloupe
Qu'est-ce qu'il y a à voir à Fermathe? Je vais y passer trois jours. Ça vaut la peine d'apporter mon appareil-photo?

Nom: Danièle
Pays: France
Pourriez-vous me donner l'adresse ou le numéro de téléphone d'un bureau touristique à Haïti? Je voudrais procurer une carte du pays et des brochures touristiques. Mille fois merci.

Nom: Claudette
Pays: Martinique
Pourriez-vous me recommander un bon hôtel au centre-ville de Port-au-Prince?

Nom: Diane
Pays: États-Unis
Une amie dont j'ai perdu l'adresse travaille à l'ambassade américaine à Port-au-Prince. Pourriez-vous me donner les coordonnées de cette ambassade?

Nom: Agnès
Pays: Espagne
Je travaille pour un magazine touristique à Barcelone. Je suis en train d'écrire un article sur les fêtes en Haïti. Quels sont les noms et les dates de vos fêtes les plus importantes?

La Guadeloupe

CAP SUD CARAIBES

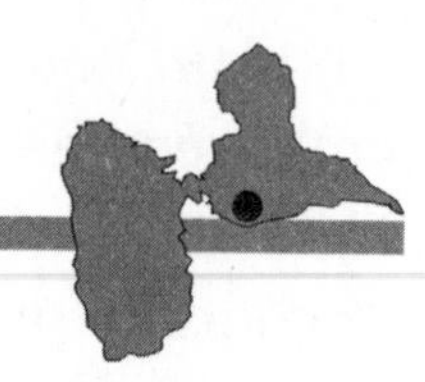

Chemin de la Plage - Petit Havre - 97190 GOSIER

Tel. (590) 85 96 02 - **Fax.** (590) 85 80 39
Directeur : Sam SITBON

Nbre de chambres : 12 chambres, "Relais Créole"
Situation : Vue sur mer et jardin, à 330 m de la plage, 15 km de l'aéroport
Ambiance : Familiale et décontractée
Equipements : Air conditionné, jardin, tél. à l'accueil
Sports et loisirs gratuits : Piscine
Prestations complémentaires : Location de voiture, snack
Langues parlées : Français / Anglais /Italien / Allemand
• Informations générales
Formule d'hébergement : CP
Tarifs Enfants : Jusqu'à 12 ans gratuit dans la chambre des parents

Deposit ou caution : 2 nuits
Annulation : 21 jours avant
Cartes de crédit : EC / MC / V
Durée séjour minimum : Non
Libération des chambres : 12 h
Animaux : Oui
Fermeture annuelle : Non
• Informations commerciales
Commercialisation :
Starter, Nouvelles Frontières, Jet Tours

U.C.P.A.

97118 SAINT-FRANÇOIS

Tél. (590) 88 64 80/88 72 05 - **Fax.** (590) 88 43 50
Télex. 919 642
Directeur : Olivier PINARD

Nbre de chambres : 60
Situation : Centre nautique au bord de mer, à côté de la Marina - Hébergement dans les hauts de St François à 1 km de la plage
Ambiance : Sportive
Equipements : Brasseur d'air, chambre de 2 ou 3 personnes
Sports et loisirs payants : Excursions
Sports et loisirs gratuits : Planche à voile (Matériel fourni : Fanatic et tiga), golf, animations, soirées

Prestations complémentaires : Bar,vélo pour chaque personne
Langues parlées : Français / Anglais
• Informations générales
Formule d' hébergement : Pension complète
Durée séjour minimum : 1 semaine
Animaux : Non
Fermeture annuelle : Non
• Restaurant
Nombre : 1
• Informations commerciales
Commercialisation :
UCPA
64, rue de la Glacière
75013 Paris

La Martinique

Le Don de la Mer
La très bonne cuisine créole
TARTANE
TRINITE
Les spécialités de "Maman Lison"
Tous les jours 12h-16h et 19h-22h
Tél: 0596.58.26.85

Location de voitures
18 agences en Martinique
Tél : 05 96 66 09 59
-20%
sur notre tarif public,
dès la Renault Twingo.
Jumbo Car
Thrifty

Passé composé des verbes réfléchis

Anne Marie Jean-Paul

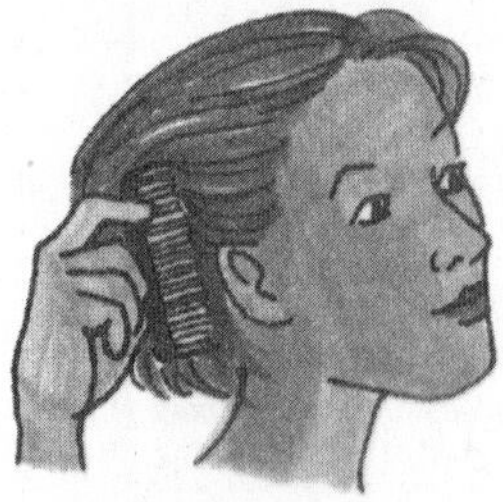

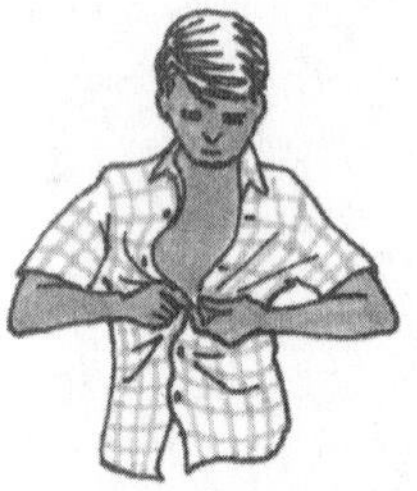

s'essuyer

se dépêcher

se raser

se regarder

se casser la jambe

se maquiller

se peigner

s'habiller

Sports I

Adja
Louis et Yves
Marc
Mireille
Daniel
Didier
Marie
Ahmed
Christiane
Olivier er Anne
Jean
Bruno
Florence

Sports II

jouer au badminton	jouer au tennis	faire de la planche à voile
jouer au basket	jouer au tennis de table	faire de la voile
jouer au cricket	aller à la pêche	faire du canoë
jouer au football	faire de l'équitation	faire du jogging
jouer au hockey	faire de la gymnastique	faire du patin à roulettes
jouer au rugby	faire de l'haltérophilie	faire du ski
jouer au squash	faire de la natation	faire du vélo

Roland Garros

Classement	Joueuse	Pays	Matchs	Aces
1	P. Schnyder	SUI	4	17
2	F. Schiavone	ITA	4	15
2	N. Vaidisova	CZE	2	15
4	K. Clijsters	BEL	4	14
5	L. Davenport	USA	5	13
5	M. Sharapova	RUS	5	13
7	E. Bovina	RUS	4	12
7	S. Kuznetsova	RUS	4	12
7	J. Henin-Hardenne	BEL	6	12
7	A. Groenefeld	GER	3	12
11	N. Petrova	RUS	6	11
11	E. Likhovtseva	RUS	6	11
13	D. Hantuchova	SVK	3	10
13	V. Zvonareva	RUS	3	10
15	C. Castano	COL	2	9
15	M. Shaughnessy	USA	1	9
15	A. Chakvetadze	RUS	3	9
18	A. Ivanovic	SCG	5	8
18	S. Mamic	CRO	2	8
20	A. Mauresmo	FRA	3	7

Films et télé

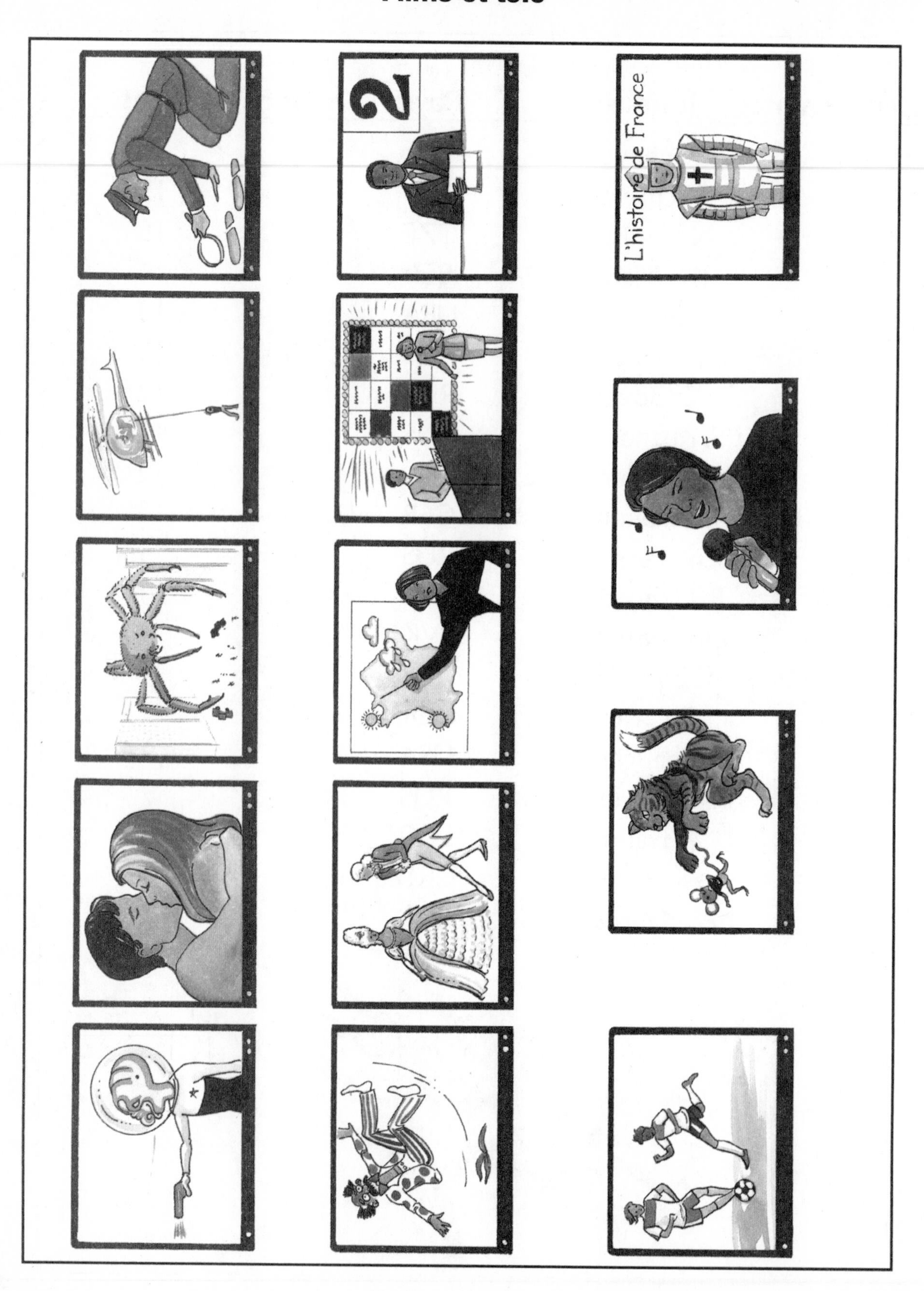

Sondage

Tu aimes ...?	J'adore ...	J'aime ...	Bof!	Je n'aime pas ...	Je déteste ...

Sam

TF1 TF1 1

Samedi 3 janvier

5.50 Le docteur mène l'enquête
Personne responsable. 9393715

6.45 TF1 info 6032609

6.55 Shopping Avenue matin 193199

7.40 Télévitrine 5165796

8.05 Téléshopping 8378661

8.55 TF! Jeunesse
Dessins animés. **Hé Arnold • Jimmy Neutron • Totally Spies • Pokemon • Infopouet.** 55896048

11.00 Les vacances de l'amour
Accident. Série. Jimmy est furieux. Il vient d'interpeller Vincent et Martin, deux jeunes gens qui terrorisent les baigneurs en faisant du jet-ski. 5710512

12.05 Attention à la marche ! 1546680
Spéciale filles-garçons. Jeu. Présentation : **Jean-Luc Reichmann.**

13.00 Journal

13.30 Reportages 948951
Bébés bleus, le cœur à l'envers. Magazine. Maternité de l'hôpital Necker à Paris. Depuis quatre mois, les médecins attendent la naissance de Louis. Ils savent que le bébé est atteint d'une malformation cardiaque congénitale.

14.05 Le trésor oublié 9875203
Téléfilm de **Gay Andrews** *(110')*. Avec : **Nicolette Sheridan** (Carrie), **Stephen Baldwin** (Bryan McBride), **Coby Ryan McLaughlin** (Carl McBride), **Hannes Jaenicke** (Ricardo Arterra), **Jerry Doyle** (le détective Sean Walker). Un incendie fait rage au Metropolitan Museum. Une équipe de pompiers lutte contre les flammes. Soudain, l'un d'eux frappe l'un de ses coéquipiers, se rue vers un camion chargé d'œuvres d'art inestimables et s'enfuit. La police se lance aussitôt à sa poursuite. Mais le véhicule perd sa cargaison avant de s'embraser.

16.00 Pacific Blue
Tourbillons. Série. Un jeune avocat de la mafia et sa femme viennent d'être assassinés dans leur maison. Seul témoin du meurtre : un garçon de six ans, né d'une ancienne liaison de l'homme de loi avec une strip-teaseuse. 2415680

16.55 Mes plus belles années
Hors-jeu. Série. Jack, au bord de la faillite, tente de rétablir ses comptes grâce aux conseils de son employé Henry. Il lui suggère d'élargir sa clientèle. 6934406

17.50 Sous le soleil 8799870
Le procès. Série. Le procès de Laure débute. Elle est défendue par Caroline. Elle a bien du mal à plaider la légitime défense pour son amie.

18.50 Qui veut gagner des millions ?
Jeu. 9108609

20.00 Journal

Nikos Aliagas en très bonne compagnie !

20.50 Présentation : **Nikos Aliagas. Divertissement.**

Star Academy : les 3 promos

Le 20 décembre dernier se déroulait la finale de la troisième promotion de la "Star Academy". Ce soir, **Nikos Aliagas** accueillent les élèves des promotions précédentes qui sont devenues, au fil des mois, des noms très connus du grand public : **Jenifer, Jean-Pascal, Nolwenn, Emma, Michal, Elodie.** Ils racontent leur parcours, les difficultés qu'ils ont pu éprouver en devant cohabiter plusieurs semaines durant au château, les relations avec les professeurs... Et puis, ensuite, la plongée dans le monde réel, les rapports avec les auteurs, les compositeurs, les musiciens, les autres artistes ! Le "conte de fée" a-t-il été de courte durée ? *Voir notre article page X.* 55097067

23.10 New York, unité spéciale
Série.

Odafin Tutuola et John Munch font face au crime

Avec : **Chris Meloni** (Elliott Stabler), **Mariska Hargitay** (Olivia Benson), **Dann Florek** (Cragen), **Richard Belzer** (John Munch), **Ice-T** (Odafin "Fin" Tutuola), **Stephanie March** (Alexandra Cabot). **Trafic d'innocence.** Le cadavre de Meredith McGrath est retrouvé dans le coffre de sa voiture. La femme a été violée puis sa bouche a été collée avec de la glue. Son bourreau s'est également rendu à son domicile, a tué son mari avant de dérober des fichiers informatiques. Stabler et Sam Bishop enquêtent sur l'affaire et tentent de comprendre ce que contenaient ces dossiers volés • **Manipulations.** Lisa, une prostituée, avoue à Benson et Stabler qu'un homme a tenté de la tuer. Les détectives finissent par avoir une idée précise de leur suspect. Ils le suivent jusqu'à un hôtel. 9484222

0.55 Les coups d'humour
Divertissement. Présentation : **Laurent Mariotte.** 1761159

Programme de la nuit

1.35 Météo 89895810

1.40 Reportages 1177094
Quelques privés bien tranquilles.

2.05 Histoires naturelles
Guinée, on n'y reste pas par hasard • Carnets algériens • Le curé chasseur. Documentaire. 79896669

4.25 Musique 8043443

5.15 Histoires naturelles 61238758
Anguilles au parapluie, un seigneur des épaves. Documentaire.

N° de la chaîne sur  N° sur  Abonnés au câble, ne pas tenir compte des numéros

 Très bon 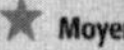 Bon ★ Moyen

Pariscope—tous les films de la semaine

SIGNIFICATION DES CODES

AN : films d'animation AV : aventure CD : comédie dramatique
CO : comédie CT : court métrage DA : dessin animé
DC : documentaire DP : drame psychologique DR : drame
FA : fantastique FD : film de danse FM : film musical FN : film noir
FP : film politique GR : guerre HO : horreur KA : karaté
PO : policier SF : science-fiction TH : thriller WS : western

A

Attention Danger Travail .... DC

B

Bye-bye Africa .... DC

C

Le Cauchemar de Darwin .... DC
Charlie et la chocolaterie .... FA
Le Château ambulant .... DA
Chicago .... FM
Chicken Little .... DA
The Constant Gardener .. FP

D

Derrida .... DC

E

L'Exorcisme d'Emily Rose . DR

G

Gentille .... CO
La Guerre des mondes (War of the Worlds) .... SF

H

Happy End .... CD
Harry Potter et la coupe de feu .... FA

J

Joyeux Noël .... DR

K

Kill Bill II .... AV
King Kong .... FA
Kirikou et les bêtes sauvages .... DA

L

Les Lionceaux .... CD
Looney Tunes passent à l'action .... DA

M

Match Point .... DR
Le Medaillon .... PO
Michel Vaillant .... AV
Million Dollar Baby ..... DR
Mission: impossible 3 .... AV
Le Monde de Narnia ..... FA
Le Mystère de la chambre jaune .... PO

N

Le Nouveau monde ..... DR

P

Palais Royal! .... CO
Le parrain (reprise) ...... DR
Pirates des Caraïbes, la Malédiction du Black Pearl .... AV

Q

Qui a tué Bambi? .... TH

R

Rencontres à Elizabethtown ...... CD
Ripoux 3 .... CO

S

Saw II .... HO
Star Wars: La Revanche des Siths .... SF
Station spatiale .... DC

T

Le Tigre et la neige ...... CO
Les Triplettes de Belleville .... DA

V

Va, vis et deviens .... DR
Variété française .... DP
La vie aquatique .... CD

W

Wallace et Gromit le mystère du lapin-garou ...... DA

Particularités

Du samedi 6 au dimanche 28 juillet, le Tour de France comprendra un prologue et 20 étapes pour une distance totale d1environ 3.300 kilomètres.
Ces 20 étapes se décomposent comme suit :
* 10 étapes dites de plaine
* 1 étape de moyenne montagne
* 6 étapes de haute montagne
* 2 étapes contre-la-montre individuel
* 1 étape contre-la-montre par équipes
* 5 arrivées en altitude
* 2 journées de repos
* 108 kilomètres contre-la-montre individuel
* 68 kilomètres contre-la-montre par équipes
* 1 transfert en avion et 1 transfert en TGV
* 21 cols de 2ème, 1ère et Hors Catégorie seront escaladés.
* 8 villes étapes inédites : Sarrebruck, Château-Thierry, Saint-Martin-de-Landelles, Bazas, Lavelanet, Vaison-la-Romaine, Bourg-en-Bresse, Régnié-Durette.

21 équipes de 9 coureurs seront invitées à participer au Tour de France. Ces équipes seront sélectionnées en deux temps selon la procédure de l'Union Cycliste Internationale applicable aux trois Grands Tours : 16 groupes sportifs qualifiés d'office fin octobre et 5 autres selon "wild cards" attribuées le 1er mai.

Les Étapes

Parcours

Étape	Date	km	Parcours
0	samedi 6 juillet	6.5 km	Luxembourg
1	dimanche 7 juillet	195	Luxembourg — Luxembourg
2	lundi 8 juillet	175	Luxembourg — Sarrebruck
3	mardi 9 juillet	185	Metz — Reims
4	mercredi 10 juillet	68	Epernay — Château-Thierry
5	jeudi 11 juillet	198	Soissons — Rouen
6	vendredi 12 juillet	198	Forges-les-Eaux — Alençon
7	samedi 13 juillet	173	Bagnoles-de-l'Orne — Avranches
8	dimanche 14 juillet	214	St Martin de Landelles — Plouay
9	lundi 15 juillet	55	Lanester — Lorient clm
R	mardi 16 juillet	-	Repos à Bordeaux
10	mercredi 17 juillet	147	Bazas — Pau
11	jeudi 18 juillet	158	Pau — La Mongie
12	vendredi 19 juillet	198	Lannemezan — Plateau de Beille
13	samedi 20 juillet	166	Lavelanet — Béziers
14	dimanche 21 juillet	220	Lodève — Le Mont Ventoux
R	lundi 22 juillet	-	Repos au Département du Vaucluse
15	mardi 23 juillet	226	Vaison-la-Romaine — Les-Deux-Alpes
16	mercredi 24 juillet	179	Les-Deux-Alpes — La Plagne
17	jeudi 25 juillet	141	Aime — Cluses
18	vendredi 26 juillet	180	Cluses — Bourg-en-Bresse
19	samedi 27 juillet	52,5	Régnié-Durette — Mâcon clm
20	dimanche 28 juillet	145	Melun — Paris-Champs-Elysées

Opéra National de Paris

du 26 octobre au 1er novembre

lundi 26 octobre
Palais Garnier - 19h30
Mats Ek-Giselle

Mats Ek-Giselle

mardi 27 octobre
Opéra Bastille - 19h30
Rigoletto
Claycomb, Pancella, Mahé, Canniccioni; Agache, Aronica, Zapater, Ferrari, Snipp, Trevisani, Testé
Direction: Carlo Rizzi

mercredi 28 octobre
Opéra Bastille - 19h
Le Chevalier à la rose
Lott, von Otter, Ziesak, Neubauer, Millot; Hawlata, Sidhom, Cassinelli, Fink, Richardson, Gahmlich, Saetre, Black, Schasching
Direction: Ulf Schirmer

Le Chevalier à la rose

jeudi 29 octobre
relâche

vendredi 30 octobre
Opéra Bastille - 19h30
Rigoletto
Claycomb, Pancella, Mahé, Canniccioni; Agache, Aronica, Zapater, Ferrari, Snipp, Trevisani, Testé
Direction: Carlo Rizzi

Rigoletto

samedi 31 octobre
Opéra Bastille - 19h
Le Chevalier à la rose
Lott, von Otter, Ziesak, Neubauer, Millot; Hawlata, Sidhom, Cassinelli, Fink, Richardson, Gahmlich, Saetre, Black, Schasching
Direction: Ulf Schirmer

dimanche 1er novembre
relâche

du 2 au 8 novembre

lundi 2 novembre
Opéra Bastille - 19h30
Rigoletto
Claycomb, Pancella, Mahé, Canniccioni; Agache, Aronica, Zapater, Ferrari, Snipp, Trevisani, Testé
Direction: Carlo Rizzi

mardi 3 novembre
Amphithéâtre Bastille - 13h
Récital-spectacle
Les artistes-stagiaires du Centre de Formation Lyrique

mercredi 4 novembre
Opéra Bastille - 19h30
Les Capulet et les Montaigu
Gallardo-Domas, Larmore; Gimenez, Kavrakos, Coliban
Direction: Bruno Campanella

Les Capulet et les Montaigu

Amphithéâtre Bastille - 18h
Passeport pour « Le Nain » et « L'Enfant et les sortilèges »

jeudi 5 novembre
Palais Garnier - 19h30
Le Nain / L'Enfant et les sortilèges Ⓝ
Le Nain: Schäfer, Anthony, Panzarella, Cals, Haidan, Karl, Creighton; Kuebler, Shore
L'Enfant...: Le Roi, Perraguin, Karl, Delunsch, Panzarella, Cals, Haidan, Rancatore; Gautier, Leguérinel, Naouri
Direction: James Conlon

Opéra Bastille - 19h30
Rigoletto
Claycomb, Pancella, Mahé, Canniccioni; Agache, Aronica, Zapater, Ferrari, Snipp, Trevisani, Testé
Direction: Carlo Rizzi

vendredi 6 novembre
Studio Bastille - 20h
Festival d'Automne à Paris

samedi 7 novembre
Opéra Bastille - 19h30
Les Capulet et les Montaigu
Gallardo-Domas, Larmore; Gimenez, Kavrakos, Coliban
Direction: Bruno Campanella

Amphithéâtre Bastille - 15h
Passeport pour « Coppélia »

dimanche 8 novembre
Palais Garnier - 15h
Le Nain / L'Enfant et les sortilèges Ⓝ
Le Nain: Schäfer, Anthony, Panzarella, Cals, Haidan, Karl, Creighton; Kuebler, Shore
L'Enfant...: Le Roi, Perraguin, Karl, Delunsch, Panzarella, Cals, Haidan, Rancatore; Gautier, Leguérinel, Naouri
Direction: James Conlon

du 9 au 15 novembre

lundi 9 novembre
Palais Garnier - 20h
Récital Thomas Hampson
Piano: Wolfram Rieger

Opéra Bastille - 19h30
Rigoletto
Claycomb, Pancella, Mahé, Canniccioni; Agache, Brown, Zapater, Ferrari, Snipp, Trevisani, Testé
Direction: Emmanuel Villaume

mardi 10 novembre
Opéra Bastille - 19h30
Les Capulet et les Montaigu
Gallardo-Domas, Larmore; Gimenez, Kavrakos, Coliban
Direction: Bruno Campanella

Amphithéâtre Bastille - 13h
Récital-spectacle
Les artistes-stagiaires du Centre de Formation Lyrique

mercredi 11 novembre
Palais Garnier - 19h30
Le Nain / L'Enfant et les sortilèges Ⓝ
Le Nain: Schäfer, Anthony, Panzarella, Cals, Haidan, Karl, Creighton; Kuebler, Shore
L'Enfant...: Le Roi, Perraguin, Karl, Delunsch, Panzarella, Cals, Haidan, Rancatore; Gautier, Leguérinel, Naouri
Direction: James Conlon

jeudi 12 novembre
Opéra Bastille - 19h30
Rigoletto
Claycomb, Pancella, Mahé, Canniccioni; Agache, Brown, Zapater, Ferrari, Snipp, Trevisani, Testé
Direction: Emmanuel Villaume

vendredi 13 novembre
Opéra Bastille - 19h30
Les Capulet et les Montaigu
Gallardo-Domas, Larmore; Gimenez, Kavrakos, Coliban
Direction: Bruno Campanella

samedi 14 novembre
Palais Garnier - 19h30
Le Nain / L'Enfant et les sortilèges Ⓝ
Le Nain: Schäfer, Anthony, Panzarella, Cals, Haidan, Karl, Creighton; Kuebler, Shore
L'Enfant...: Le Roi, Perraguin, Karl, Delunsch, Panzarella, Cals, Haidan, Rancatore; Gautier, Leguérinel, Naouri
Direction: James Conlon

Opéra Bastille - 19h30
Rigoletto
Claycomb, Pancella, Mahé, Canniccioni; Agache, Brown, Zapater, Ferrari, Snipp, Trevisani, Testé
Direction: Emmanuel Villaume

dimanche 15 novembre
relâche

La Veuve joyeuse

du 16 au 22 novembre

lundi 16 novembre
relâche

Pina Bausch - Le Sacre du printemps

mardi 17 novembre
Opéra Bastille - 19h30
Rigoletto
Claycomb, Pancella, Mahé, Canniccioni; Agache, Brown, Zapater, Ferrari, Snipp, Trevisani, Testé
Direction: Emmanuel Villaume

Amphithéâtre Bastille - 20h
Festival d'Automne à Paris

mercredi 18 novembre
Palais Garnier - 19h30
Le Nain / L'Enfant et les sortilèges Ⓝ
Le Nain: Schäfer, Anthony, Panzarella, Cals, Haidan, Karl, Creighton; Kuebler, Shore
L'Enfant...: Le Roi, Perraguin, Karl, Delunsch, Panzarella, Cals, Haidan, Rancatore; Gautier, Leguérinel, Naouri
Direction: James Conlon

jeudi 19 novembre
relâche

vendredi 20 novembre
Palais Garnier - 19h30
Le Nain / L'Enfant et les sortilèges Ⓝ
Le Nain: Schäfer, Anthony, Panzarella, Cals, Haidan, Karl, Creighton; Kuebler, Shore
L'Enfant...: Le Roi, Perraguin, Karl, Delunsch, Panzarella, Cals, Haidan, Rancatore; Gautier, Leguérinel, Naouri
Direction: James Conlon

Opéra Bastille - 19h30
Rigoletto
Claycomb, Pancella, Mahé, Canniccioni; Agache, Brown, Zapater, Ferrari, Snipp, Trevisani, Testé
Direction: Emmanuel Villaume

samedi 21 novembre
Palais Garnier - 19h30
Spectacle de ballets
Duboc / Graham / Bausch
Direction: Guillaume Tourniaire

Opéra Bastille - 19h30
La Veuve joyeuse
von Stade, Galstian, Martikke, Palzer, Lilova; Hagegard, Jones, Kmentt, Trevisani, Schwanbeck, Cale Johnson, Alofs, Kraemmer
Direction: Armin Jordan

dimanche 22 novembre
Palais Garnier - 20h30
Musique de chambre
Ramsøe, Beethoven, Haendel, Tomasi, Bruckner, Janáček
Par les musiciens de l'Orchestre de l'Opéra National de Paris

Bercy

CALENDRIER CONCERTS

DÉCEMBRE
Le 21 décembre – BLACK EYED PEAS

JANVIER
Du 13 au 29 janvier – MYLÈNE FARMER

FÉVRIER
Du 21 au 23 février – DEPECHE MODE

MARS
Le 18 mars – LA NUIT DE SAINT PATRICK

AVRIL
Le 04 avril – EROS RAMAZZOTTI

MAI
Le 15 mai – SANTANA
Le 19 mai – TEXAS

SEPTEMBRE
Les 29 & 30 septembre – JOHNNY HALLYDAY

Instruments I

Instruments II

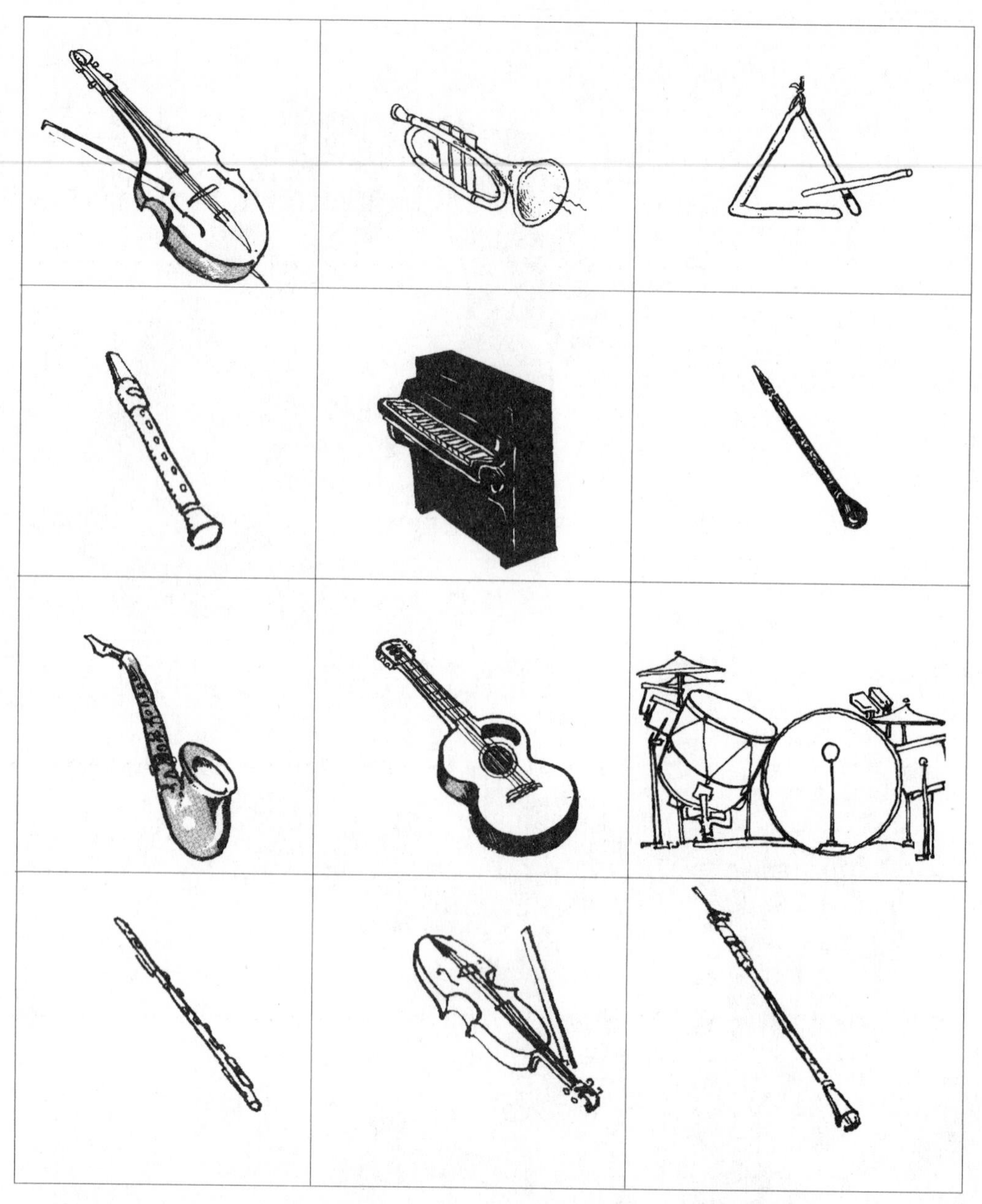

jouer de la batterie
jouer de la clarinette
jouer de la flûte
jouer de la flûte à bec
jouer de la guitare
jouer de la trompette

jouer du hautbois
jouer du piano
jouer du saxophone
jouer du triangle
jouer du violon
jouer du violoncelle

Passe-temps

aller à la maison des jeunes
aller à la pêche
aller à la piscine
aller au cinéma
aller au théâtre
aller à une discothèque
collectionner des timbres
danser
écouter de la musique
faire de l'escalade
faire des mots croisés
faire une promenade
jouer aux cartes
jouer aux échecs
lire
prendre des photos
regarder la télévision
DISCO

Maison des Jeunes et de la Culture—Evry

Activités adolescents

Place Général de Gaulle
BP 715
91001 Evry, France
Tél. 01 60 77 33 94
Fax 01 69 36 34 19
Internet http://perso.wanadoo.fr/mjc.evry
E-mail MJC.evry@wanadoo.fr

Atelier Guitare

avec Patrice BATTIONI
à partir de 13 ans :
samedi 14 h - 15h 30, par séquence de 20 mn / personne
Guitare électrique dans le style rock, blues et jazz

Atelier Musical

avec Patrice BATTIONI
à partir de 13 ans :
vendredi 18 h 30 - 20 h
Apprentissage du jeu en groupe

Atelier Percussions

avec Steeve ROSSARD & Jean-Charles PERRAULT
à partir de 13 ans :
débutants : mercredi 18 h 30 - 20 h
perfectionnement : mardi 18 h 30 - 20 h
S'initier aux sonorités et rythmes afros pour acquérir une pratique instrumentale: le Djembé.

Atelier Batterie

avec Philippe LORETZ
à partir de 13 ans :
samedi 10 h - 12 h par séquence de 20 mn par personne

Un local Musique à la MJC

Nous avons le plaisir de vous annoncer que la MJC est en mesure d'accueillir les groupes désireux de répéter sur Evry. Nous mettons à votre disposition un local de 25 m2 entièrement rénové et insonorisé. Toutes les conditions sont donc réunies pour satisfaire de nombreux groupes. Une pièce supplémentaire est également prévue pour entreposer votre matériel. N'hésitez pas à contacter Claire pour convenir des jours et des heures qui vous seront réservés.

À la poste

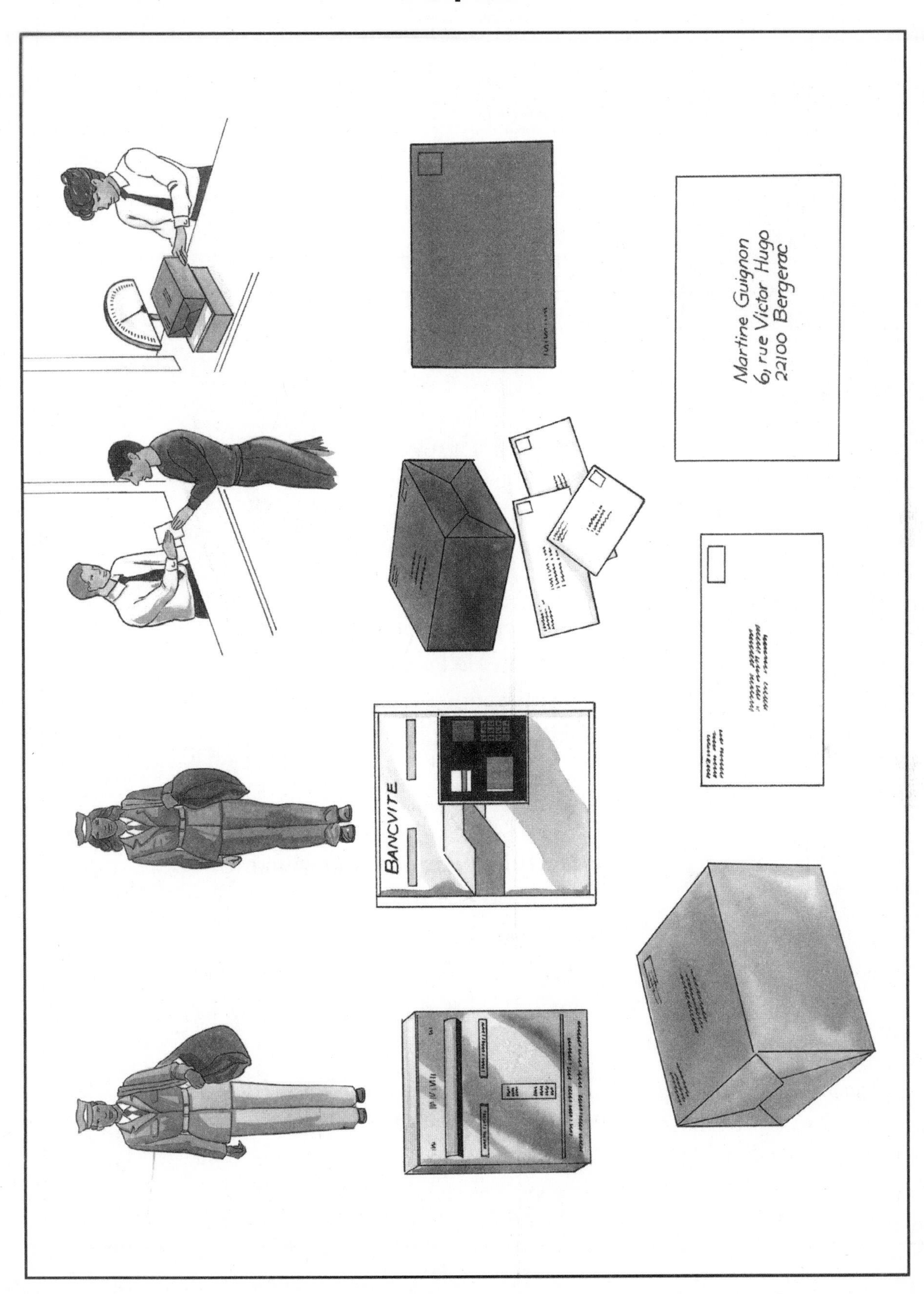

Timbres français

Timbre Séparation des Églises et de l'État : 0.53€
Réf. 1105012
05.12.05
Format : 26 x 40 mm - Feuille de 50 TP
Ce timbre est émis pour célébrer le centenaire de cette loi marquant la séparation des Églises et de l'État.

Timbre Emission commune France / République Tchèque : 0.55€
Réf. 1105002
06.05.05
Format : 40 x 30 mm - Feuille de 42 TP
On célèbrera le 2 décembre 2005 le bicentenaire de la bataille d'Austerlitz. L'occasion d'une émission commune République Tchèque - France.

Timbre Jules Verne - Cinq semaines en ballon : 0.53€
Réf. 1105912
30.05.05
Format : 21 x 36 mm - Feuille de 50 TP
Ce timbre est issu du bloc "Les voyages extraordinaires de Jules Verne" et illustre son roman "Cinq semaines en ballon".

Bijoux

La Bijouterie GOLDMINE
76,07€
24795
Bague martelée or jaune
60,83€
24559
Boucles d'oreilles martelées or jaune
304,750€
24599045
Collier maille grain de café or jaune
121,81€
24599018
Bracelet maille grain de café or jaune
45,58€
25166
Bague martelée or jaune
bouscule les prix !
76,07€
24775045
Collier pendentif coeur or jaune
39,48€
24633
Pendentif soleil or jaune
30,34€
24884
Boucles d'oreilles soleil or jaune
137,05€
18331042
Collier maille corde or jaune
152,30€
24591018
Bracelet maille palmier or jaune
152,30€
18048018
Bracelet maille americaine or jaune
76,07€
18331018
Bracelet maille corde or jaune

Strasbourg

■ FLANERIES DANS LE PARC DE L'ORANGERIE
(entrée gratuite)
Illumination tous les soirs de juin à mi-septembre dès la tombée de la nuit jusqu'à 23 h 30.
Sonorisation d'ambiance de juin à mi-septembre les samedis et dimanches de 20 h à 22 h.

VISITE GUIDEE PLACE DE LA CATHEDRALE

■ PROMENADES SUR L'ILL ET LE RHIN
• Promenades en bateau organisées par le Port Autonome de Strasbourg
15, rue de Nantes
☎ 03.88.84.13.13 - Fax : 03.88.84.33.13
sur l'Ill : (avec commentaire) toute l'année, durée 1 h 15, prix : 5,64€, tarif réduit (enfants < 3 ans, étudiants, militaires) : 2,97€
Départs "flâneries nocturnes" à 21 h 30 et 22 h, du 1er mai au 3 octobre prix : 5,95€,
tarif réduit : 3,13€
sur le Rhin : départ promenade Dauphine (sauf jours fériés) : du 1er juillet au 4 septembre
Départ à 14 h 30, durée 3 h, prix : 7,93€, tarif réduit : 3,96€.
• Promenades gastronautiques à bord des bateaux-restaurants Alligator et Nymphe de l'Ill.
☎ 03.88.84.10.01 - Fax : 03.88.34.55.38
Tarif : 10,67€ (croisière) + menu à partir de 17,53€.

■ CROISIERES SUR LE RHIN
S'adresser à : Alsace-Croisières
12, rue de la Division-Leclerc - 67000 Strasbourg
☎ 03.88.76.44.44 - Fax : 03.88.32.49.96
Prix : 29,73€ (pour croisière d'un jour)
croisière sur le Danube en 6 ou 7 jours.

■ PROMENADES EN MINI-TRAIN DANS LE VIEUX STRASBOURG (durée 45 mn).
Du 1er avril au 1er novembre sauf le 1er mai.
Départ place du Château (côté sud cathédrale)
Réservations : CTS - ☎ 03.88.77.70.03.
Fax : 03.88.77.70.99 - Prix : 4,12€ - Groupe 20 personnes : 3,20€ - Enfants < 12 ans : 2,29€

■ PLANETARIUM DE STRASBOURG ET EXPOSITIONS THEMATIQUES
Renseignements sur le programme du jour et réservations :
Planétarium de Strasbourg - 4, rue de l'Observatoire
☎ 03.88.21.20.40 - Fax : 03.88.21.20.45

■ MARCHE AUX PUCES
- Brocante tous les mercredis et samedis.
place du Vieil-Hôpital (près de la cathédrale).
- Marché aux livres les mercredis et samedis : place Gutenberg.

■ VISITE DE BRASSERIES (gratuit)
- HEINEKEN - contacter le service des visites
10, rue Saint-Charles
67300 Schiltigheim - ☎ 03.88.19.58.00
- KRONENBOURG - contacter le service des visites
68, route d'Oberhausbergen
67200 Strasbourg - ☎ 03.88.27.41.59
- METEOR - contacter le service des visites
6, rue du Général-Lebocq
67270 Hochfelden - ☎ 03.88.71.73.73

■ LE PASSEPORT TOURISTIQUE
"STRASBOURG PASS" pour individuels donne droit entre autres à la gratuité de plusieurs visites (tour en bateau, spectacle son et lumière à la cathédrale, musée, montée sur la plate-forme de la cathédrale...) et le demi-tarif pour certaines autres visites.
Il est valable 3 jours. Vendu à l'Office du Tourisme de Strasbourg, tarif : 7,62€.

Bijoux et accessoires

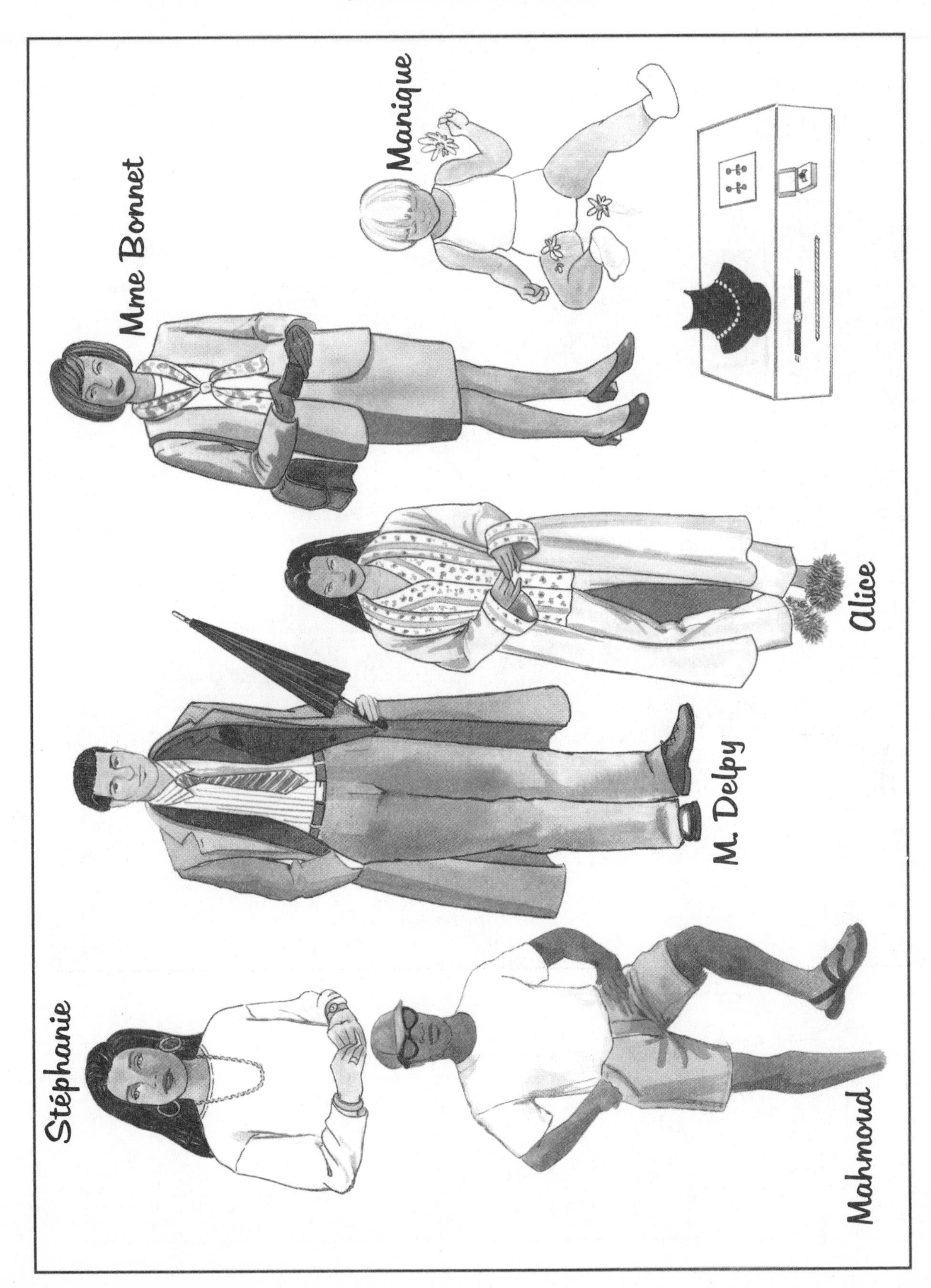

Qu'est-ce qu'elles portent?

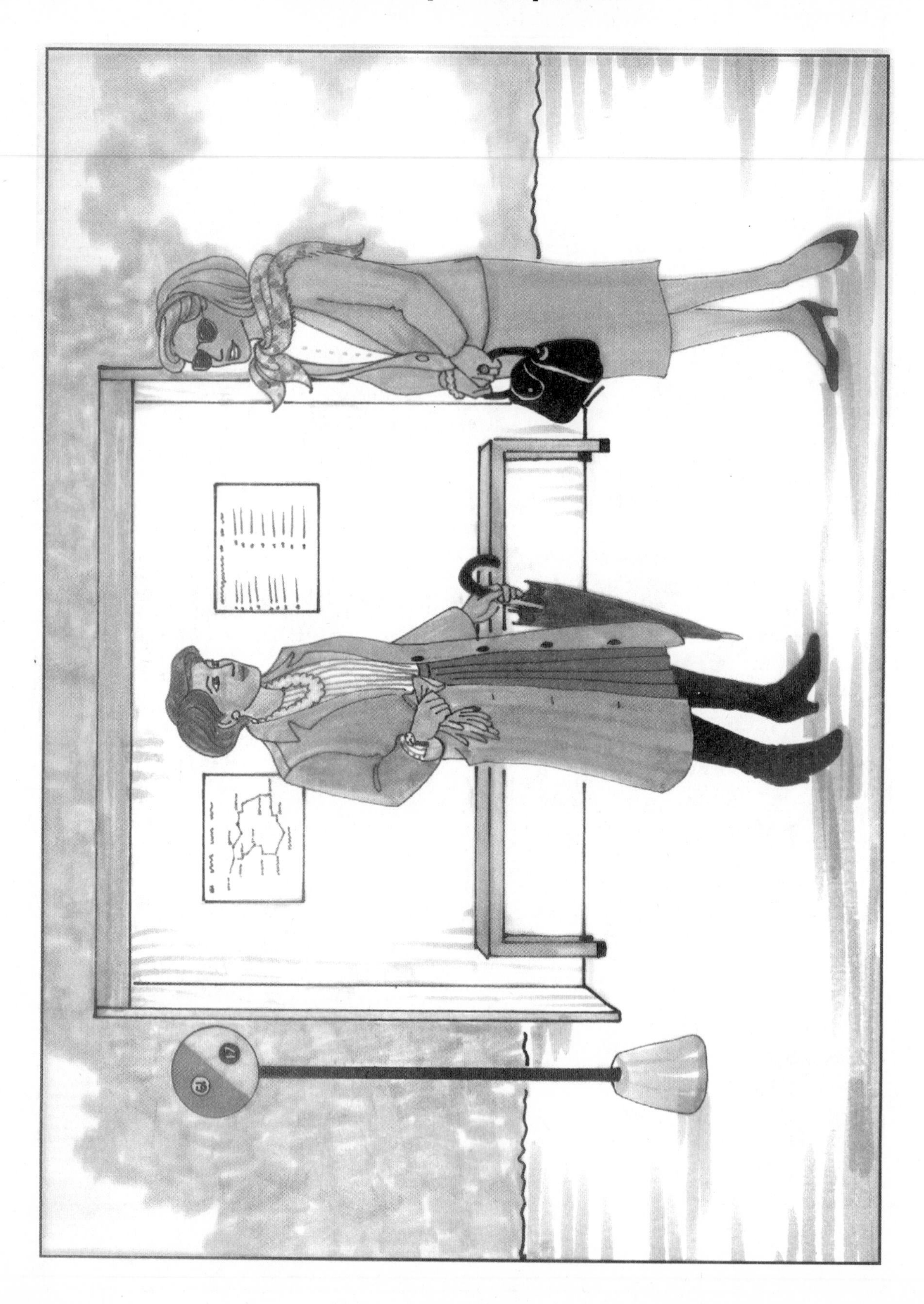

Objets personnels

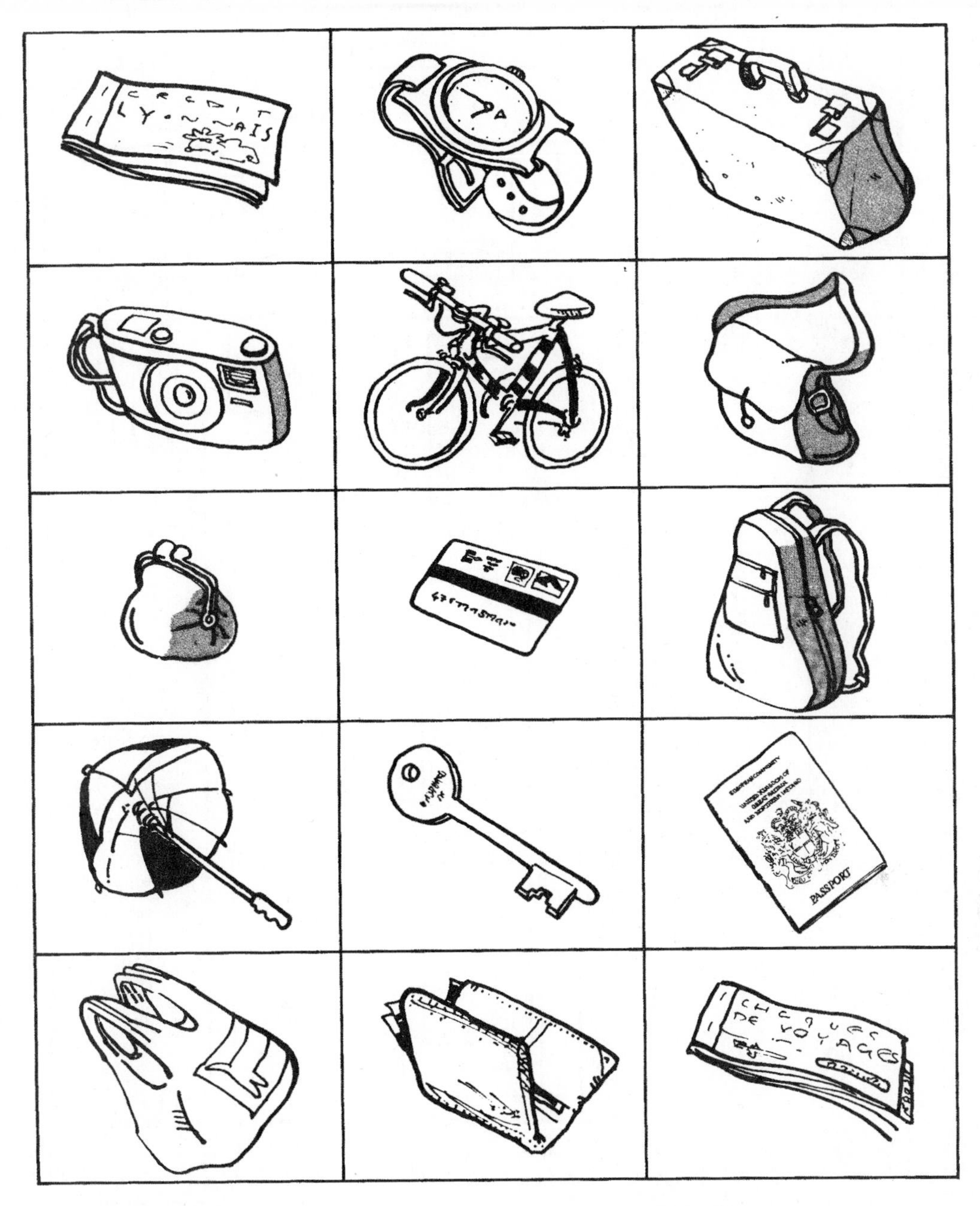

un appareil-photo
un carnet de chèques
une carte de crédit
des chèques de voyage
une clé
une montre
un parapluie
un passeport
un portefeuille
un porte-monnaie
un sac à dos
un sac à main
un sac en plastique
une valise
un vélo

Galeries Lafayette

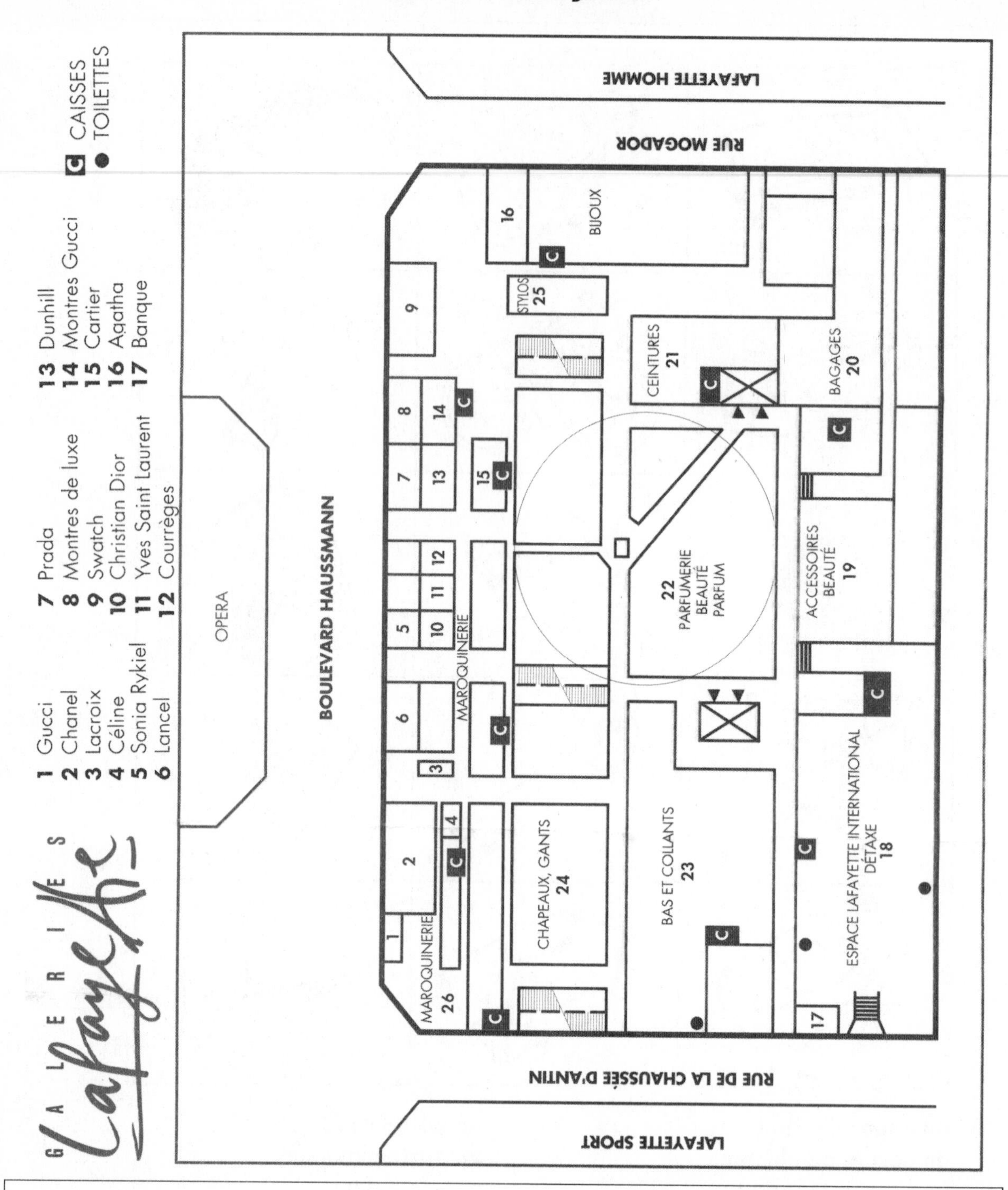

1- What is the price?
Quel est le prix?

2- Where is the nearest cashier
Où est la caisse la plus proche?

3- Could you direct me to the Espace International?
Pourriez-vous me diriger vers l'Espace International s'il vous plait?

4- Please contact an interpreter.
Veuillez contacter une interprète.

5- Where are the restrooms?
Où sont les toilettes?

Le Maghreb

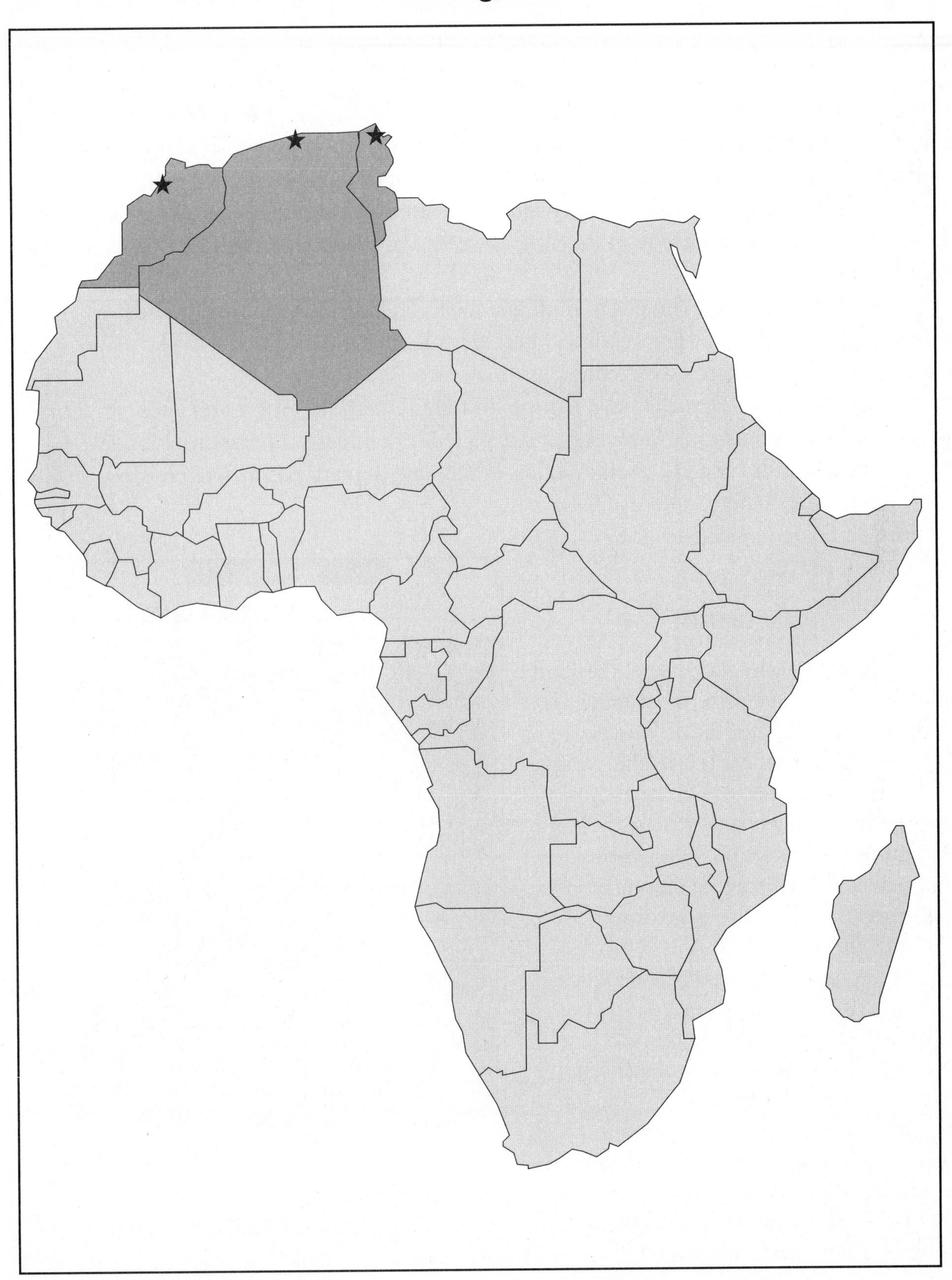

Culture algérienne

Rencontres et mariage

Les jeunes Algériens se rencontrent à l'université, dans les lieux publics et à certaines occasions, mais ils se donnent aussi rendez-vous comme en Occident. Le mariage ne représente pas seulement l'union de deux individus, mais aussi celle de deux familles. Les parents sont par conséquent étroitement impliqués dans le choix des conjoints. Les femmes se marient généralement vers l'âge de 20 ans, les hommes un peu plus tard.

Il était traditionnellement normal que trois générations au moins (grands-parents, enfants mariés et leurs épouses) partagent la même maison, mais dans les villes la famille nucléaire est devenue plus fréquente.

Les rôles de l'homme et de la femme sont clairement définis: les femmes s'occupent des enfants et de la maison, tandis que les hommes sont responsables des revenus de la famille et de la discipline. Les enfants ne doivent pas mettre en cause l'autorité de leurs parents et doivent les prendre en charge lorsque ceux-ci deviennent plus âgés.

Viande

Couscous aux deux viandes

Plat unique

STUDIO X

À table

Dans les villes, la cuisine d'origine française côtoie la cuisine algérienne traditionnelle. Le produit de base de l'alimentation dont est fait le plat typique se dit "seksul" en berbère et "couscous" dans les autres régions d'Afrique du Nord. Il s'agit de semoule cuite à la vapeur servie avec de l'agneau ou du poulet et des légumes, souvent sous la forme d'un ragoût.

Les musulmans, respectueux des interdits rituels, ne mangent pas de porc et ne boivent pas d'alcool.

Bien que les Algériens utilisent habituellement des couverts à table, on mange encore certains plats avec les doigts, surtout ceux qui sont accommodés de sauces riches, où le pain fait office de cuillère.

La main gauche étant utilisée traditionnellement pour l'hygiène corporelle, on fait usage de la seule main droite lorsque l'on mange sans couverts.

Raï

Avant, le raï était chanté essentiellement dans les souks, les mariages et les circoncisions. Vers les années 50, avec la chanteuse Remitti, cette musique commence à rassembler quelques chanteurs pour finir par s'étendre à toute l'Algérie après l'indépendance. Mais c'est seulement au début des années 80 que le raï va véritablement être catapulté au rang de musique nationale avec l'arrivée de nouveaux chanteurs: les «Chebs.» Chebs signifie «jeune homme.» Le régime Algérien réprouve cette nouvelle musique ainsi que les Chebs qui y mélangent instruments traditionnels, synthétiseurs, batterie électronique et basse, remettant au goût du jour de vieilles mélodies.

Les figures emblématiques de cette nouvelle génération sont Khaled, le «Roi» et chef de file; Mami, le «Dauphin»; Chaba Zahouania, à la voix blues; ou Raïna Raï, groupe au son très «Dire Straits.» Le raï rencontre un tel succès que le premier festival raï a lieu à Oran en 1985. C'est à cette époque que, face à un tel engouement, le pouvoir Algérien «nationalise» le raï.

1986 Le raï arrive en France. Peu de gens achète des disques de raï. C'est Cheb Mami qui va ouvrir les portes des distributeurs en lançant un album.

1990 Cheb Mami, premier chanteur raï à s'être produit aux États-Unis, sort l'album «Let me Raï,» enregistré à Los Angeles. Son impact est tel parmi le public qu'il sera même repris par Haïm Moshé, chanteur populaire israélien. Les titres raï sont de plus en plus travaillés et arrangés en studio gagnant ainsi en qualité musicale et sonore.

1992 La guerre civile fait rage en Algérie. Khaled explose le Top 50 avec «Didi,» arrangé par Don Was, alors que Cheb Hasni devient le leader du mouvement Raï Love.

1996 En octobre, Khaled remet ça avec «Aïcha,» écrit par Jean-Jacques Goldman et interprété en français. Rachid Taha, de son côté, sort «Ya Rayah» (album Diwan), un mélange rock techno oriental. Un jeune garçon de 20 ans fait son apparition en enregistrant l'album «Baïda.» Le premier single à tourner sur les ondes est «Tellement N'Brick» qui va littéralement pulvériser le classement des meilleures ventes. Ce jeune garçon que l'on va surnommer «Le petit Prince du raï» s'appelle Faudel.

1998 «Un, deux, trois… soleils» fait son apparition à la demande d'Universal qui met ainsi en scène trois vedettes: Khaled, Rachid Taha et Faudel. Le 26 septembre, 17 000 spectateurs viennent à Bercy pour les écouter accompagnés d'une formation égyptienne sous la direction de Steve Hillage et d'un orchestre occidental. Des milliers de personnes restent sur les marches de l'entrée faute de places. Un CD et une vidéo du spectacle sortent deux mois plus tard. L'album est vendu à plus de 300 000 exemplaires et devient disque de platine tandis que Faudel obtient le Prix de la révélation musique 99.

Carte d'identité de la Tunisie

Jours fériés

- 1er janvier (Jour de l'An),
- 20 mars (fête de l'Indépendance),
- 21 mars, (fête de la Jeunesse),
- 9 avril (fête des Martyrs),
- 1er mai (fête du Travail),
- 25 juillet (fête de la République),
- 13 août (fête de la Femme),
- 7 novembre (Commémoration du 7 novembre 1987).

Les fêtes musulmanes sont mobiles et les dates, arrêtées en fonction des phases de la lune. Le début du ramadan évolue de 11 jours chaque année : il débutera cette année vers le 17 novembre. L'Aïd el Fitr (fin décembre/début janvier).

Principales fêtes

En juillet et août des festivals sont organisés dans toutes les régions : concerts, théâtres, arts populaires, notamment à Carthage, Bizerte, Tabarka, Sousse, Monastir et Mahdia...

A noter :

- Course croisière Port Grimaud-Monastir (début juillet).
- Festival International du Jazz à Tabarka (29 juin-7 juillet).
- Festival des éponges à Zarzis (été).
- Festival de musique symphonique à El Jem (fin juillet).
- Festival de la plongée sous-marine à Tabarka (septembre).
- Fête des dates à Kebili (octobre).
- Festival international des oasis à Tozeur (novembre).

Moyenne des températures

	Tunis	désert
janvier	11°	12°
avril	15/16°	20°
juillet	26°	32°
octobre	20/21°	22°
décembre	12°	12°

Shopping au Maroc

Le souk, qui pourrait être l'équivalent du marché en France, est un lieu extrêmement important dans la vie marocaine ; on peut en voir dans toutes les villes du royaume.

Le souk permet bien sûr d'acheter des produits, mais c'est aussi un lieu important des relations sociales ; c'est au souk que se règlent les litiges, les emprunts, et aussi les projets de mariages.

A l'origine, le souk permettait aux différentes tribus de se rencontrer en terrain neutre. Pour les touristes, le souk est un endroit incontournable qui permet de se plonger pleinement dans l'ambiance marocaine et de prendre la température du pays.

Bien entendu, les touristes sont repérés à 100 mètres par les vendeurs et autres rabatteurs.... Vous vous ferez donc normalement, gentiment harceler, sachez le prendre avec philosophie, soyez ferme, prenez le temps de regarder et négocier, cela fait partie du jeu.

Le souk est une source de revenu importante pour les artisans du royaume, aussi y trouve-t-on de tout et n'importe quoi dans un véritable bazar organisé (c'est le souk!). Tapis, souvenirs, ornementations, alimentation, guides, épices, babouches, art traditionnel....

Le souk, c'est tout le charme et l'hospitalité du Maroc réunis en un seul lieu.

Euros

1
EURO CENT

2
EURO CENT

5
EURO CENT

10
EURO CENT

20
EURO CENT

50
EURO CENT

1
EURO

2
EURO

20
20 EURO

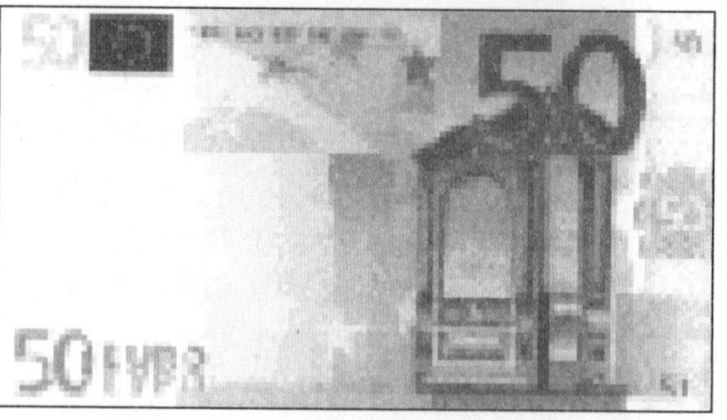
50
50 EURO

100
100 EURO

5
5 EURO

200
200 EURO

10
10 EURO

500
500 EURO

À l'aéroport I

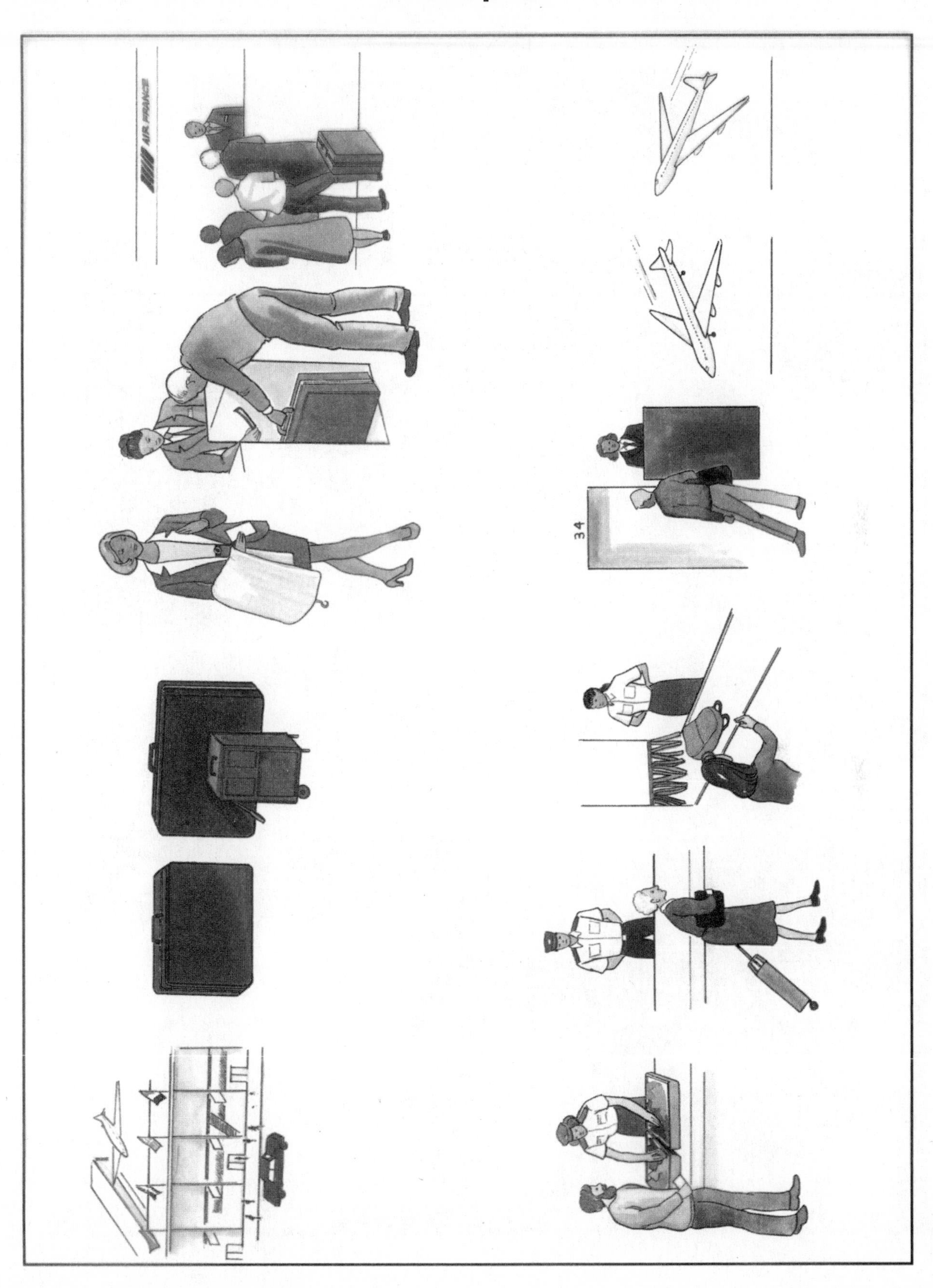

À l'aéroport II

BAGAGES ÉGARÉS AIR FRANCE

Nom: ______________________________
Prénom: ______________________________
Nationalité: ______________________________
Adresse: ______________________________
Ville: ______________________________
Code postal: ______________________________
Pays: ______________________________
Numéro de téléphone: ______________________________

Adresse en France: ______________________________
Numéro de téléphone en France: ______________________________

Date: ______________________________
Numéro de vol: ______________________________
En provenance de: ______________________________

Description des valises:

_____ petite(s)	_____ moyenne(s)	_____ grande(s)
_____ noire(s)	_____ bleue(s)	_____ grise(s)
_____ marron	_____ verte(s)	_____ rouge(s)

Description du contenu (vêtements, accessoires, affaires de toilette, etc.)
____
____
____
____

Valeur totale du contenu (en euros): ______________________________

Signature: ______________________________
Date: ______________________________

À la gare I

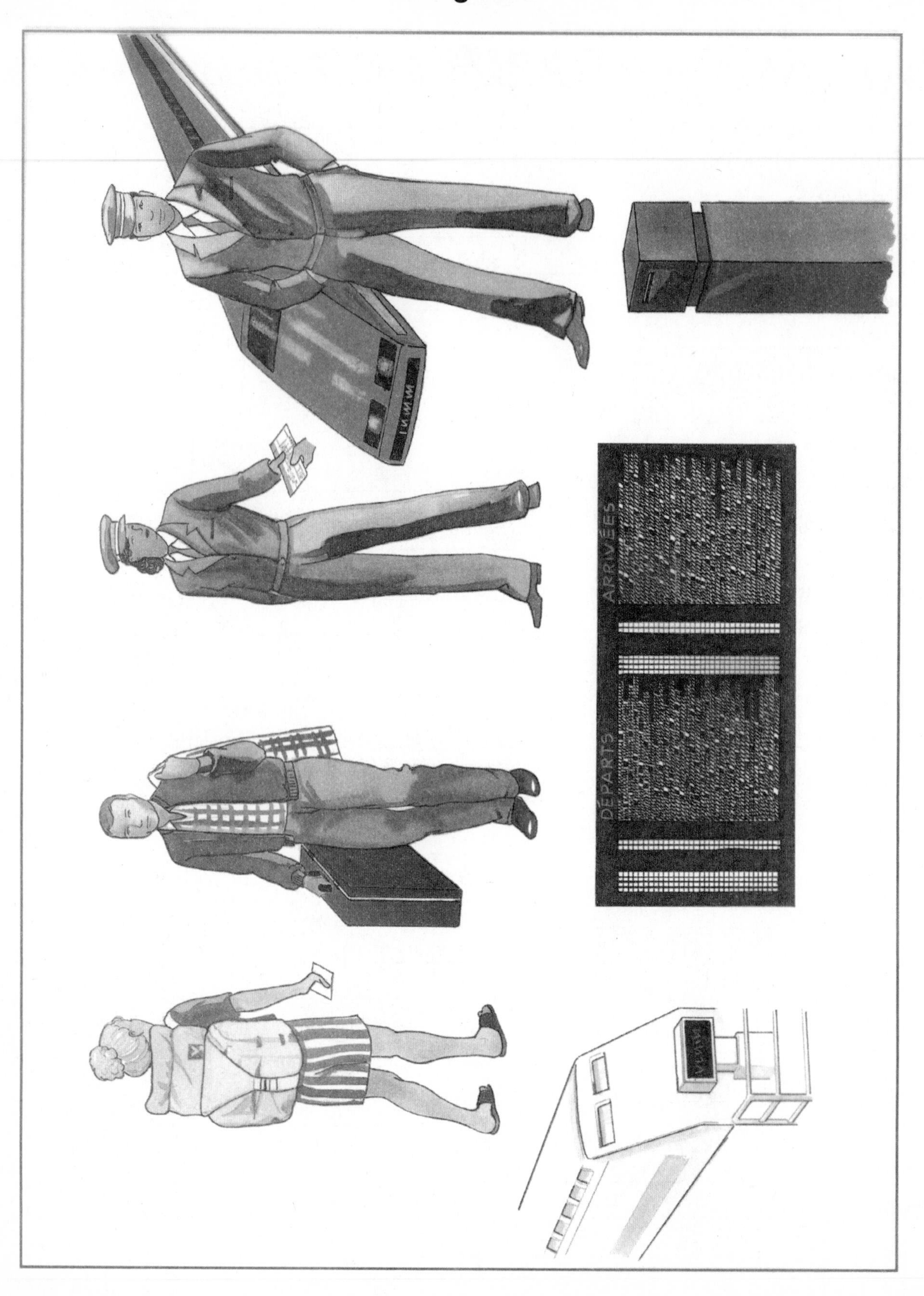

À la gare II

Horaire des trains II

Tours → Vendôme → Paris

PRIX

[1] [3] *Pour connaître le prix de votre billet*
[2] [4] *consultez le tableau pages 60 à 62*
[ ] ***TGV** ne circulant pas ce jour-là.*

HORAIRES

N° du TGV		8200	8202	8308	8414	540/1	8420	8222	8328
Particularités						✱	✱	✱	✱ (3)
Tours	D	6.36	7.04	a	a	a	a	12.09	a
Saint-Pierre-des-Corps	D	6.42	7.10	8.17	9.42	10.08	10.49	12.16	13.14
Vendôme-Villiers-sur-Loir	D		7.32					12.37	
Massy	A					10.58			
Paris-Montparnasse 1-2	A	7.40	8.15	9.15	10.40		11.45	13.20	14.10

SEMAINES TYPES

		8200	8202	8308	8414	540/1	8420	8222	8328
Du 23 mai au 02 juillet et du 30 août au 25 septembre	**Lundi**	3	4	4	3	1	4	1	4
	Mardi	1	4	4	4	1	1	1	1
	Mercredi	1	4	4	4	1	1	1	1
	Jeudi	1	4	4	4	1	1	1	1
	Vendredi	1	4	2	3	1	1	1	3
	Samedi		1	1	3	1		1	1
	Dimanche			1	1	1		1	1
Du 03 juillet au 29 août	**Lundi**	1	3	4	3	1	3	1	1
	Mardi	1	1	1	4	1	1	1	1
	Mercredi	1	1	1	4	1	1	1	1
	Jeudi	1	1	1	4	1	1	1	1
	Vendredi	1	1	1	3	1	1	1	3
	Samedi		1	1	1	1		1	1
	Dimanche			1	1	1		1	1

JOURS PARTICULIERS

		8200	8202	8308	8414	540/1	8420	8222	8328
MAI	Dimanche 30			1	1	1		1	1
	Lundi 31			1	1	1		1	3
JUIN	Mardi 1er	3	3	4	4	1	4	1	4
JUILLET	Mercredi 14			1	1	1		1	1
	Vendredi 30	1	1	1	1	1	3	3	3
	Samedi 31		1	1	3	1		3	3
AOUT	Samedi 28		1	1	3	1		3	3
	Dimanche 29			1	1	1		3	3

D Départ A Arrivée

a Correspondance à St-Pierre-des-Corps par navette.

(1) Ne prend pas de voyageurs pour Massy.
(2) Circule à partir du 30 août les lundis, mardis, mercredis, jeudis et samedis [1].
(3) Du 23 mai au 02 juillet départ St-Pierre-des-Corps 12.59 arrivée Paris 13.55.

✱ Espaces "Carré" réservables, en priorité, par les voyageurs "Kiwi" et les voyageurs accompagnés d'enfants.

Châteaux de la Loire

BLOIS

La construction du château s'est effectuée à quatre époques. D'abord il repose sur l'ancien château féodal des Comtes de Blois. Louis XII fit construire l'aile nord-est entre 1498 et 1508 sous la direction de Colin Biart, l'architecte du Château d'Amboise.

L'architecte de l'aile nord-ouest, dite François I, est Dominique de Cortone; elle est marquée par la Renaissance italienne. La façade sur cour est agrémentée du célèbre escalier de style gothique.

La façade nord domine l'ancienne vallée de l'Arrou et comporte de nombreuses galeries et fenêtres. L'aile sud-ouest est due à Gaston d'Orléans; elle est restée inachevée.

Le château de Blois a souvent servi de résidence royale au XVIème siècle, c'est là qu'eut lieu l'assassinat du Duc de Guise en 1588. La mère de Louis XIII, Marie de Médicis y fut exilée pendant deux ans en 1617.

CHAMBORD

Chambord a été construit à la demande de François Ier à partir de 1519; il se situe au sud de la Loire à une quinzaine de kilomètres de Blois. Sa dimension et son envergure sont impressionnants. Il a été édifié en plusieurs fois et a nécessité un chantier de près de 2000 ouvriers pendant plus de 12 ans. Il a été achevé sous Henri III.

Ce château est l'œuvre de plusieurs architectes dont Jacques Sourdeau et son neveu, Pierre Neveu, ainsi que Jacques Coqueau. Il a abrité de nombreux séjours royaux sous Henri II, François II, Charles IX et Louis XIII.

En 1746 le Roi Louis XV le donna au Maréchal de Saxe en récompense des services rendus à la France.

Chenonceaux

CHAMBRE DE DIANE DE POITIERS

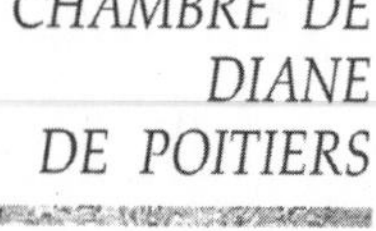

La Chambre de Diane de Poitiers

Cette pièce fut la chambre de la favorite du Roi Henri II, Diane de Poitiers, à laquelle il avait fait don de Chenonceau.

En 1559, à la mort d'Henri II, tué en combat singulier lors d'un tournoi par le Capitaine de ses gardes écossais Gabriel Montgomery, sa veuve Catherine de Médicis, se fit restituer Chenonceau par Diane et lui donna en échange Chaumont-sur-Loire.

LA CHEMINÉE de Jean Goujon, sculpteur français de l'Ecole de Fontainebleau, porte (ainsi que le plafond à caissons) les initiales d'Henri II et Catherine de Médicis : H et C qui entrelacées pouvaient former le D de Diane de Poitiers.

DEUX TAPISSERIES DES FLANDRES DU XVIème SIÈCLE, aux dimensions considérables, représentent :

- LE TRIOMPHE DE LA FORCE, montée sur un char tiré par deux lions, et environnée de scènes de l'Ancien Testament.

Dans la bordure supérieure, la phrase latine se traduit par «Celui qui aime de tout son cœur les dons célestes, ne recule pas devant les actes que la Piété lui dicte».

- LE TRIOMPHE DE LA CHARITÉ, figurée sur un char, tenant dans sa main un cœur et montrant le soleil, entourée d'épisodes bibliques. La devise latine se traduit ici par : «Celui qui montre un cœur fort dans les périls, reçoit à sa mort, comme récompense, le Salut».

A gauche de la fenêtre, **«VIERGE À L'ENFANT» par MURILLO**.

A droite de la cheminée, toile de l'Ecole Italienne du XVIIème Siècle : «Le Christ dépouillé de ses vêtements».

Sous cette toile, une bibliothèque renferme **LES ARCHIVES DE CHENONCEAU** dont un exemplaire, exposé dans la vitrine, permet de reconnaître les signatures de Thomas Bohier et Diane de Poitiers.

Les fauteuils Henri II sont recouverts de cuir de Cordoue.

Le Triomphe de la Charité

LA GALERIE

La Galerie

De la chambre de Diane de Poitiers, on rejoint **LA GALERIE** par un petit passage.

En 1576, d'après les plans de Philibert de l'Orme, Catherine de Médicis fait construire une galerie sur le pont de Diane de Poitiers.

Longue de 60 mètres, large de 6 mètres, éclairée de 18 fenêtres, avec son sol carrelé de tuffeau et d'ardoise et son plafond à solives apparentes, c'est une magnifique salle de bal.

Elle fut inaugurée en 1577 lors des fêtes données par Catherine de Médicis en l'honneur de son fils le Roi Henri III.

A chaque extrémité, deux très belles **CHEMINÉES RENAISSANCE**, dont l'une n'est qu'un décor entourant la porte Sud qui mène à la rive gauche du Cher.

Les médaillons sur les murs furent rajoutés au XVIIIème Siècle et représentent des personnages célèbres.

Durant la Première Guerre Mondiale, Monsieur Gaston Menier propriétaire de Chenonceau, fit aménager à ses frais, **UN HÔPITAL** dont les différents services occupaient toutes les salles du Château.

Lors de la Seconde Guerre Mondiale, de nombreuses personnes mirent à profit la situation privilégiée de la Galerie, dont la porte Sud donnait accès à la **ZONE LIBRE**, alors que l'entrée du Château se trouvait en zone occupée.

La Galerie transformée en hôpital

Envoi de cartes postales par e-mail

Envoyez une carte postale virtuelle à un(e) ami(e). Suivez (*follow*) ces instructions:

1. Allez à ce site sur Internet: http://www.francebalade.com/cards/isend.php3.
2. Choisissez d'abord une photo d'un château que vous avez étudié.
3. Remplissez (*fill in*) le nom et l'adresse e-mail du destinaire (*addressee*).
4. Remplissez votre nom et votre adresse e-mail.
5. Écrivez votre message.
    - Écrivez la date.
    - Saluez (*greet*) votre ami(e).
    - Parlez de votre voyage en train.
    - Décrivez le château que vous avez visité.
    - Donnez un fait (*fact*) historique du château.
    - Signez votre nom.
6. Cliquez sur «Prévisualiser» pour obtenir (*obtain*) le look de votre carte postale.
7. Cliquez encore (*again*) pour envoyer la carte postale.

Versailles

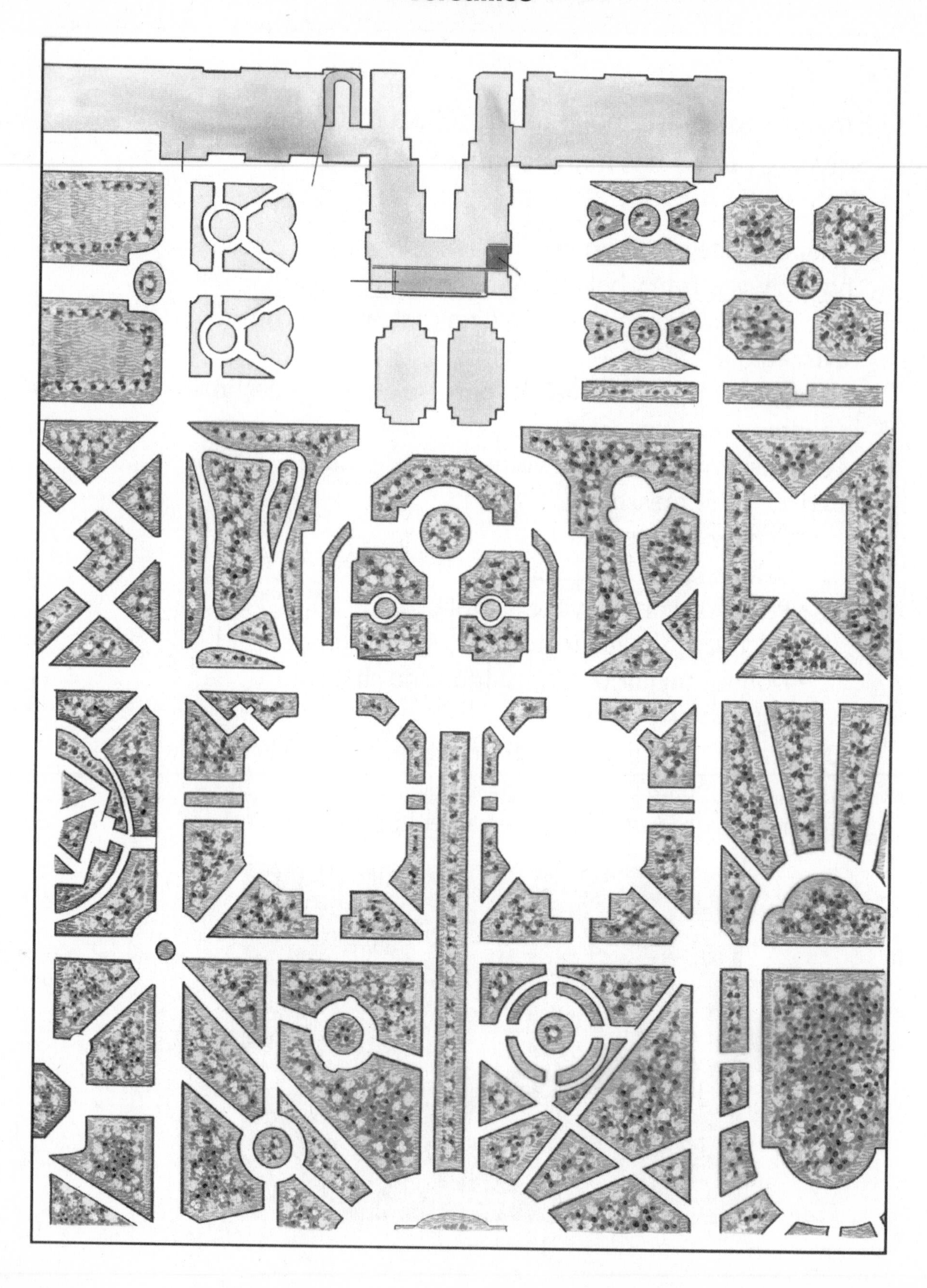

Hôtels à Versailles

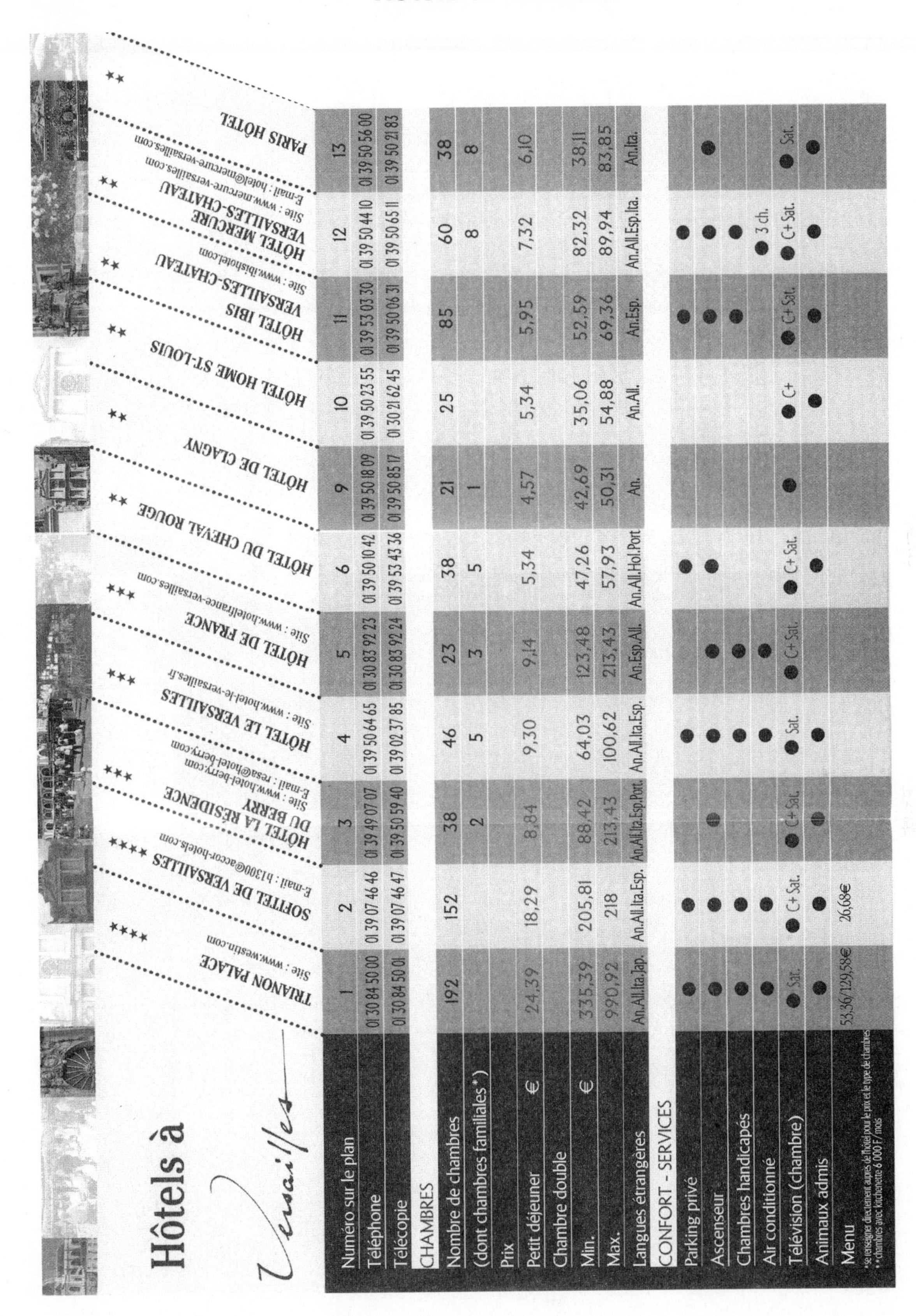

Hôtels à Versailles

	TRIANON PALACE ★★★★ Site : www.westin.com	SOFITEL DE VERSAILLES ★★★★ E-mail : h1300@accor-hotels.com	HÔTEL LA RÉSIDENCE DU BERRY ★★★ Site : www.hotel-berry.com E-mail : resa@hotel-berry.com	HÔTEL LE VERSAILLES ★★★ Site : www.hotel-le-versailles.fr	HÔTEL DE FRANCE ★★★ Site : www.hotelfrance-versailles.com	HÔTEL DU CHEVAL ROUGE ★★	HÔTEL DE CLAGNY ★★	HÔTEL HOME ST-LOUIS ★★	HÔTEL IBIS VERSAILLES-CHATEAU ★★ Site : www.ibishotel.com	HÔTEL MERCURE VERSAILLES-CHATEAU ★★ Site : www.mercure-versailles.com E-mail : hotel@mercure-versailles.com	PARIS HÔTEL ★★
Numéro sur le plan	1	2	3	4	5	6	9	10	11	12	13
Téléphone	01 30 84 50 00	01 39 07 46 46	01 39 49 07 07	01 39 50 64 65	01 30 83 92 23	01 39 50 10 42	01 39 50 18 09	01 39 50 23 55	01 39 53 03 30	01 39 50 44 10	01 39 50 56 00
Télécopie	01 30 84 50 01	01 39 07 46 47	01 39 50 59 40	01 39 02 37 85	01 30 83 92 24	01 39 53 43 36	01 39 50 85 17	01 30 21 62 45	01 39 50 06 31	01 39 50 65 11	01 39 50 21 83
CHAMBRES											
Nombre de chambres	192	152	38	46	23	38	21	25	85	60	38
(dont chambres familiales*)			2	5	3	5	1			8	8
Prix											
Petit déjeuner €	24,39	18,29	8,84	9,30	9,14	5,34	4,57	5,34	5,95	7,32	6,10
Chambre double											
Min. €	335,39	205,81	88,42	64,03	123,48	47,26	42,69	35,06	52,59	82,32	38,11
Max.	990,92	218	213,43	100,62	213,43	57,93	50,31	54,88	69,36	89,94	83,85
Langues étrangères	An.All.Ita.Jap.	An.All.Ita.Esp.	An.All.Ita.Esp.Port.	An.All.Ita.Esp.	An.Esp.All.	An.All.Hol.Port	An.	An.All.	An.Esp.	An.All.Esp.Ita.	An.Ita.
CONFORT - SERVICES											
Parking privé	●	●		●		●			●	●	
Ascenseur	●	●	●	●	●	●			●	●	●
Chambres handicapés	●	●		●	●				●	●	
Air conditionné	●	●		●	●					● 3 ch.	
Télévision (chambre)	● Sat.	● C+ Sat.	● C+ Sat.	● Sat.	● C+ Sat.	● C+ Sat.	●	● C+	● C+ Sat.	● C+ Sat.	● Sat.
Animaux admis	●	●	●	●		●		●	●	●	●
Menu	53,36/129,58€	26,68€									

*se renseigner directement auprès de l'hôtel pour le prix et le type de chambres
**chambres avec kitchenette 6 000 F/mois

Lettre pour réserver une chambre d'hôtel

(Adresse)

Hôtel Château Laurier
695, Grande Allée Est
Québec, Qc
Canada, G1R 2K4
......................, 20......

Monsieur ou Madame,

Je vous serais obligé(e) de me communiquer vos conditions et tarifs pour un séjour de .... nuits du .... jusqu'au .... (*dates*).

Nous sommes ...... adultes et ...... enfants, âgés de ...... et ...... ans.

Je voudrais réserver .... chambres à un lit (avec bain/douche).
.... chambres à deux lits (avec bain/douche).
.... chambres à grand lit (avec bain/douche).

Nous désirons la pension complète.
la demi-pension.
la chambre et le petit déjeuner seulement.

Veuillez trouver ci-joint un coupon-réponse international.

Je vous prie de croire, Monsieur ou Madame, à l'expression de mes sentiments distingués.

(Signature)

Symboles des services hôteliers

ascenseur
avec douche
avec salle de bains
bords de mer, rivière ou lac
chambres accessibles aux handicapés physiques
chiens admis
chiens non admis
forêt
groupes
ouvert toute l'année
parking
piscine
restaurant
salon pour séminaires
téléphone dans les chambres
télévision dans les chambres

Déclaration d'arrivée à l'hôtel

Déclaration d'arrivée

Date d'arrivée	
Date probable de départ	
Nom de famille	
Prénom	
Date de naissance	
Nationalité	
Adresse (rue, numéro)	
Code postal	
Nombre d'enfants	
Signature du client(e)	

Facture d'hôtel

HÔTEL CHÂTEAU LAURIER
695, GRANDE ALLÉE EST
QUÉBEC, QC
CANADA, G1R 2K4

Le .... Chambre No ....

No.004813
Avez-vous déposé votre clé?

MONTANT		
Téléphone		
Taxe séjour		
TOTAL		

Hôtel Château Laurier

L'HÔTEL CHÂTEAU LAURIER A PENSÉ À TOUT AFIN QUE VOTRE SÉJOUR SOIT PARFAIT.

154 chambres climatisées dont
- 9 avec foyer au bois et bain thérapeutique
- Accès Internet gratuit

- Service de télécopie
- Stationnement gratuit avec service de voiturier
- Télévision par satellite
- Restaurant Le Patrimoine
- Salle à manger
- Bar salon
- Trois salles de réunion avec vidéoconférence
- Coffrets de sûreté
- Tabagie, journaux
- Tours de ville Gray Line

PÉRIODE	1 LIT QUEEN	2 LITS SIMPLES	2 LITS DOUBLES
1 jan. - 31 jan.	79$ - 89$	89$	99$
1 fév. - 2 fév.*	99$ - 109$	109$	119$
3 fév. - 7 fév.*	79$ - 89$	89$	99$
8 fév. - 9 fév.*	99$ - 109$	109$	119$
10 fév. - 14 fév.	79$ - 89$	89$	99$
15 fév. - 16 fév.	109$ - 129$	129$	139$
17 fév. - 30 avril	79$ - 89$	89$	99$
1 mai - 5 juil.	99$ - 109$	109$	119$
6 juil. - 20 oct.	109$ - 129$	129$	139$
21 oct. - 26 déc.	79$ - 89$	89$	99$
27 déc. - 31 déc.	99$ - 109$	109$	119$

PÉRIODE	1 LIT QUEEN	2 LITS DOUBLES	1 LIT KING	1 LIT KING DE LUXE	1 LIT KING SALON
1 jan. - 31 jan.	109$	119$ - 129$	129$ - 139$	169$	149$ - 169$
1 fév. - 2 fév.*	129$	139$ - 149$	159$ - 169$	199$	179$ - 199$
3 fév. - 7 fév.*	109$	119$ - 129$	129$ - 139$	169$	149$ - 169$
8 fév. - 9 fév.*	129$	139$ - 149$	159$ - 169$	199$	179$ - 199$
10 fév. - 14 fév.	109$	119$ - 129$	129$ - 139$	169$	149$ - 169$
15 fév. - 16 fév.	149$	159$ - 169$	179$ - 189$	249$	219$ - 239$
17 fév. - 30 avril	109$	119$ - 129$	129$ - 139$	169$	149$ - 169$
1 mai - 5 juil.	129$	139$ - 149$	159$ - 169$	199$	179$ - 199$
6 juil. - 20 oct.	149$	159$ - 169$	179$ - 189$	259$	229$ - 239$
21 oct. - 26 déc.	109$	119$ - 129$	129$ - 139$	169$	149$ - 169$
27 déc. - 31 déc.	129$	139$ - 149$	159$ - 169$	199$	179$ - 199$

* *Ces tarifs spéciaux ne sont pas en vigueur durant la dernière fin de semaine du Carnaval de Québec.*

La Citadelle/Musée du Royal 22e Régiment
Côte de la Citadelle C. P. 6020, succursale
Haute-Ville, Québec G1R 4V7
(418) 694-2815
http://www.lacitadelle.qc.ca/

La Citadelle constitue, au sommet du cap Diamant, le flanc est des fortifications de Québec. Elle fait de la ville, le «Gibraltar d'Amérique.» Sa construction débutant en 1820, s'échelonne sur plus de 30 ans et présente un plan en étoile caractéristique des fortifications à la Vauban. La tradition militaire y est assurée par **la Retraite** et la **Relève de la Garde** durant la période estivale (horaire à vérifier au 694-2815). L'ensemble est accessible lors des **visites commentées. Horaire:** tous les jours; avril à mi-mai, 10 h à 16 h. Mi-mai et juin, 9 h à 17 h. Juillet à la fête du Travail, 9 h à 18 h. Septembre, 9 h à 16 h. Octobre, 10 h à 15 h. Novembre à avril, sur réservation de groupe. **Entrée:** adultes: 5,50$; âge d'or: 4 $; enfants (7 à 17 ans): 2,75 $; (6 ans et moins) accompagnés d'un parent ainsi que les handicapés: gratuit. Tarif familial: 13,75 $ (maximum). Information en français, anglais, allemand, espagnol, italien, mandarin et japonais.

Aux Anciens Canadiens

Nos Plats Principaux	Table d'hôte	À la carte
Viandes et Volailles		
Médaillons de dindon grillés, sauce au parfum de noisettes	27.50$	18.50$
Suprême de poulet en feuilleté à la façon des Artisans et son velouté	28.50$	19.50$
Filet d'agneau grillé, sauce à la menthe et au sherry	31.00$	22.00$
Mignon de bœuf, sauce à l'oseille et au "vin caribou"	36.50$	27.50$
Spécialités Québécoises		
Régal de Grand-père: Ragoût de pattes de cochon et de boulettes	28.00$	19.00$
Coureur des Bois: Tourtière du Lac St-Jean et son mijoté de bison	33.00$	24.00$
Assiette du Pays: Tourtière du Québec, ragoût de boulettes, grillades de lard salé et fèves au lard	28.00$	19.00$
Bouilli québécois de boeuf, lard salé et légumes	28.00$	19.00$
Poisson et Fruits de mer		
Brochette de thon mariné au romarin, sauce au vin rouge et champignons sauvages	33.50$	24.50$
Filet de saumon frais, cuit en pâte feuilletée et son velouté de crevettes	31.00$	22.00$
Fruits de mer à notre façon: crevettes et pétoncles mijotés à l'échalote, au vin blanc et à la crème, queue de homard grillée	54.00$	45.00$
Gibiers		
Bourguignon de caribou à la crème et au vin DuBleuet	34.00$	25.00$
Les trois mignons: Caribou, bison et cerf, grillé, sauce au cognac et poivre rose	46.00$	37.00$
Magret de canard braisé au sirop d'érable	32.00$	23.00$
Suprême de faisan grillé, vieux cheddar et sauce aux pleurotes	38.00$	29.00$
Plat Végétarien		
Jardinière de légumes frais, mijotés à la manière d'antan	25.50$	16.50$

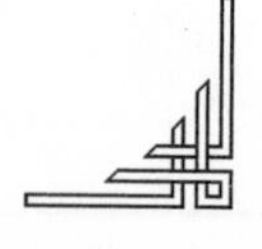

Sainte-Anne-de-Beaupré

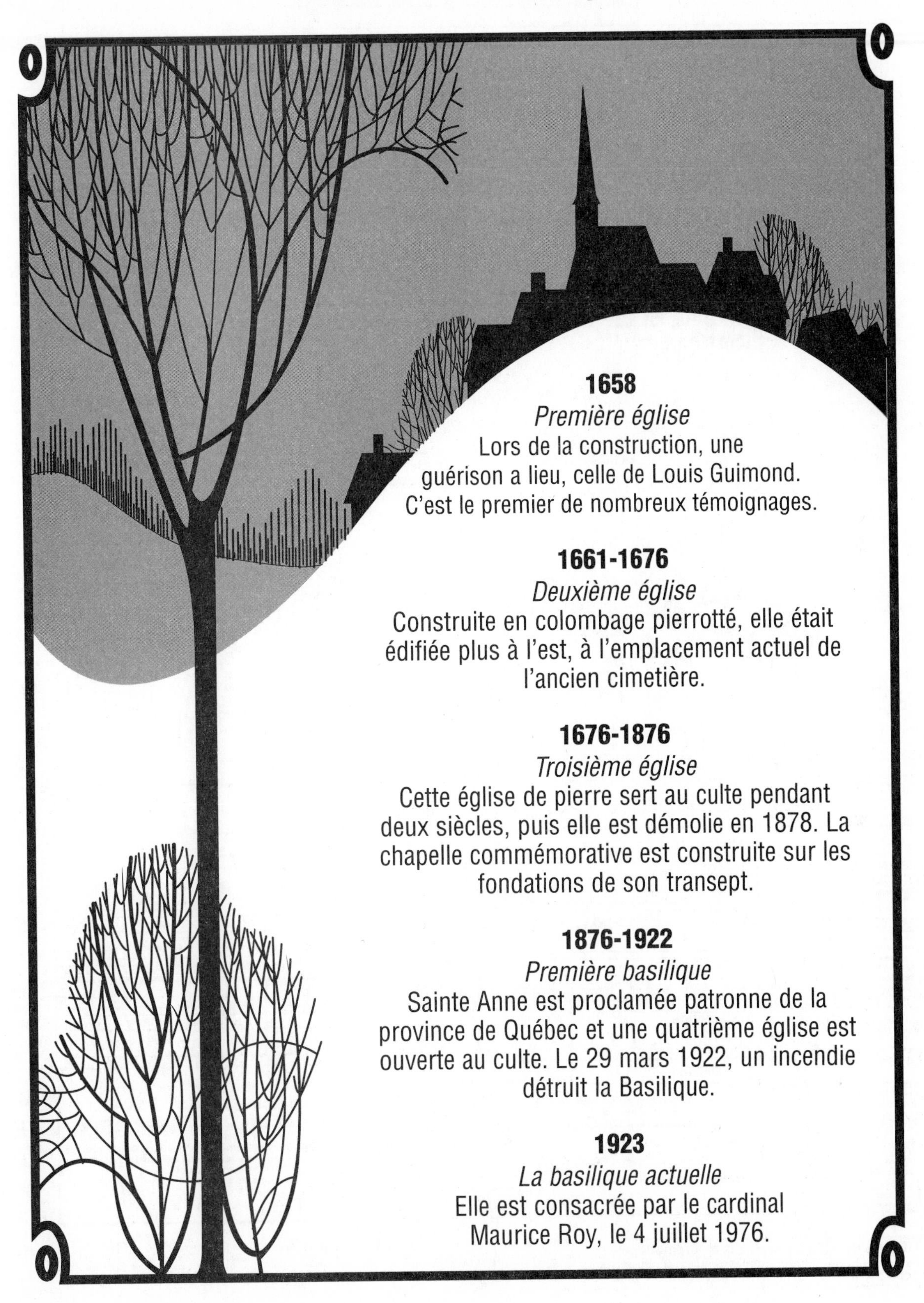

1658

Première église

Lors de la construction, une guérison a lieu, celle de Louis Guimond. C'est le premier de nombreux témoignages.

1661-1676

Deuxième église

Construite en colombage pierrotté, elle était édifiée plus à l'est, à l'emplacement actuel de l'ancien cimetière.

1676-1876

Troisième église

Cette église de pierre sert au culte pendant deux siècles, puis elle est démolie en 1878. La chapelle commémorative est construite sur les fondations de son transept.

1876-1922

Première basilique

Sainte Anne est proclamée patronne de la province de Québec et une quatrième église est ouverte au culte. Le 29 mars 1922, un incendie détruit la Basilique.

1923

La basilique actuelle

Elle est consacrée par le cardinal Maurice Roy, le 4 juillet 1976.

Auberges de jeunesse

6000 Auberges dans le monde et dans 62 pays, 220 Auberges en France, 80 activités sportives toute l'année, 17 stations de ski, 50 destinations à l'étranger, des week-end détente, des stages linguistiques, etc

POUR ALLER PARTOUT EN FRANCE ET DANS LE MONDE, PAYEZ MOINS CHER ET PASSEZ PAR NOS DEUX CASES DÉPART : STOP BY ANY OF THE FOLLOWING FUAJ OFFICES FOR THE BEST SERVICES AT THE LOWEST PRICE :

FUAJ
Centre Fédéral
27, rue Pajol 75018 Paris
Tél. : 01 44 89 87 27
3615 code FUAJ
Métro : La Chapelle

La Boutique des AJ
9, rue Brantôme 75003 Paris
Tél. : 01 48 04 70 40
Métro : Rambuteau ou Les Halles

Auberge de Jeunesse "Le d'Artagnan"
80, rue Vitruve 75020 Paris
Tél. : 01 40 32 34 53
Métro : Pte de Bagnolet

Auberge de Jeunesse "Jules Ferry"
8, bd Jules Ferry 75011 Paris
Tél. : 01 43 57 55 60
Métro : République ou Goncourt

Auberge de Jeunesse "Cité des Sciences"
1, rue Jean-Baptiste-Clément
93310 Le-Pré-St-Gervais
Tél. : 01 48 43 24 11
Métro : Hoche

"Léo Lagrange"
107, rue Martre
92110 Clichy
Tél. : 01 41 27 26 90
Métro : Mairie de Clichy

LES AUBERGES, C'EST TOUT UN MONDE !

POUR EVITER AFFLUENCE ET ATTENTE, PRENDS VITE TA CARTE F.U.A.J. !

BULLETIN D'ADHESION INDIVIDUELLE *
(à remplir en caractères d'imprimerie)

Désignation	PRIX
Cotisation annuelle	€
Surprime Ski	€
FFCC : vignette camping à apposer sur carte d'A.J. (vignette valable en France seulement)	€
Carnet camping international/FICC (1) N°.............. (1 vignette internationale/FICC de l'année comprise) (1)	€
FICC. vignette internationale à apposer sur carnet camping international/FICC	€
TOTAL..................	€

(1) Le Carnet de Camping international et la vignette FICC sont **COMPLEMENTAIRES** à la vignette FFCC de l'année en cours, apposée sur la carte d'A.J. ou la carte camping (individuelle ou familiale).

NOM
PRENOM
ADRESSE (N°, nom de la rue)
PROFESSION — Code — voir liste des codes ci-dessous
LOCALITÉ, lieudit ou autres indications utiles
DATE DE NAISSANCE — Cocher la case — SEXE F M
CODE POSTAL
Bureau PTT distributeur
LIEU DE NAISSANCE
NATIONALITE 17

▽ COCHER LA CASE CORRESPONDANTE
J'AI MOINS DE ☐ 18 ans ☐ 26 ans
J'AI PLUS DE ☐ 26 ans
J'AI ADHERE L'ANNEE DERNIERE
☐ OUI ☐ NON

Codes - Catégories socio-professionnelles

10 - Etudiants et Elèves de Grandes Ecoles.
11 - Scolaire et Lycéens.
12 - Professeurs.
13 - Instituteurs.
14 - Employés de bureau des secteurs public et privé.
15 - Personnel para-médical et hospitalier.
16 - Ouvriers : contremaître et ouvriers qualifiés et spécialisés des secteurs public et privé, apprentis divers, manoeuvres, marins, mineurs, etc...
17 - Cadres moyens.
18 - Cadres supérieurs.
19 - Artisans, Commerçants.
20 - Agriculteurs.
21 - Sans profession (mères de famille, etc...)
22 - Autres catégories : personnels de service, artistes, militaires, etc...
23 - Chômeurs.

*** La carte délivrée est annuelle et internationale.**
Elle est strictement personnelle et non transmissible.
Aucun duplicata ne sera délivré en cas de vol, perte, etc...

Fait à.. le ....
Signature de l'adhérent
Signature des Parents (obligatoire pour les mineurs)

Auberge de jeunesse

Fiche.....

No. de passeport ....

Carte d'A. J. no. ....

NOM..

Prénom..

Né le...

Adresse. ....

....

Nationalité..

Nombre de personnes..

Expressions québécoises

Vocabulaire

Au Québec	En France
avoir du bacon	être riche
avoir du fonne	s'amuser
balayeuse (f.)	aspirateur (m.)
bloc d'appartements (m.)	immeuble (m.)
bonjour	au revoir
breuvage (m.)	boisson (f.)
cave (f.)	sous-sol (m.)
cédule (f.)	emploi du temps (m.)
cheap	bon marché
chum(me)	copain/copine
coke (m.)	coca (m.)
courriel (m.)	e-mail (m.)
crème glacée (f.)	glace (f.)
déjeuner	prendre le petit déjeuner
dîner	déjeuner
dumb	bête
étatsunien(ne)	américain(e)
faire le barda	faire le ménage
fèves vertes (f.)	haricots verts (m.)
hambourgeois (m.)	hamburger (m.)
lessiveuse (f.)	machine à laver (f.)
loyer (m.)	appartement (m.)
magasin à rayons (m.)	grand magasin (m.)
mouiller	pleuvoir
napkin (f.)	serviette (f.)
pain doré (m.)	pain perdu (m.)
parade (f.)	défilé (m.)
patate (f.)	pomme de terre (f.)
pois verts (m.)	petits pois (m.)
rôtie (f.)	pain grillé (m.)
running (m.)	basket (f.)
shampou (m.)	shampooing (m.)
souper	dîner
théâtre (m.)	cinéma (m.)
venter	faire du vent
vivoir (m.)	salon (m.)

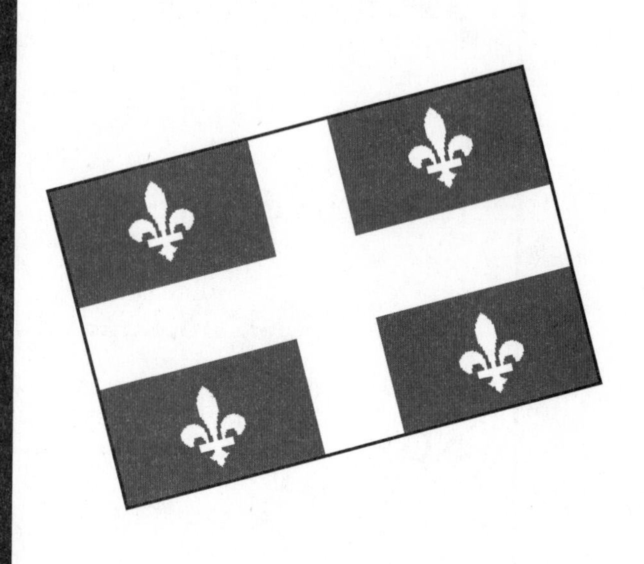

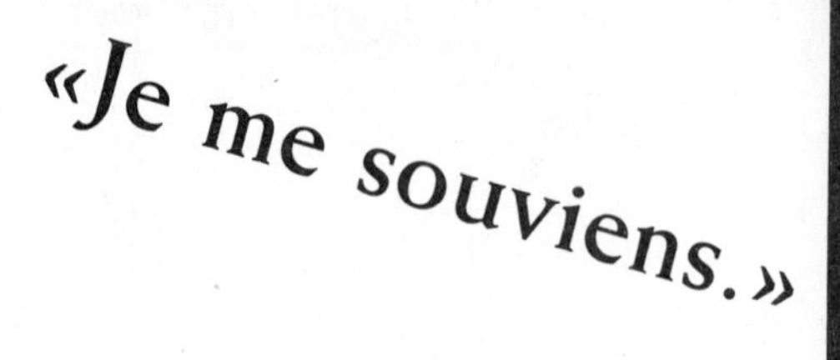

Expressions

C'est hallucinant.	Far out.
C'est une patate chaude.	It's a hot potato (issue).
Citron.	Aw, darn it.
Il est un granola.	He's a health food nut.
Il n'est pas un gros char.	He's not too bright.
Je fake.	I'm pretending.
Je suis cassé(e) comme un clou.	I'm flat broke.
Je suis dans le jus.	I'm crazy busy.
Je suis dans mes bonnes.	I'm in good shape.
Je suis en frais de....	I'm busy doing....
Je suis loqué(e).	I'm lucky.
L'affaire est chocolat.	It's in the bag.
Lâche pas la patate.	Don't quit now.
T'as raté.	You blew it.
T'es au max.	You're the best.
T'es chic and swell.	You're looking good.
Tiguidou.	Perfect.

Place Ville-Marie

Vêtements - dames

Boutique L'Officiel
Chelsea
Dynamite Boutique
Joenette
Laura
Laura Petites
Manteaux Manteaux
Reitmans
Tristan & Iseut
Underworld

Vêtements - hommes

America

Vêtements - enfants

Triks

Bijouteries

Ardene
Bijouterie Orly
Montre-Al
Oh Folies

Chaussures

Ashton
Chaussures Brown's
Chaussures Dack
Chaussures François Villon
Chaussures French
Chaussures FX Lasalle
Chaussures Mayfair
Chaussures Simard & Voyer
Moneysworth & Best Quality
Shoe Repair

Sports

Joenette

Cuirs, valises

Cuirs Danier
Jovin

Cadeaux, livres, papeterie, cartes de souhaits

Bowring
Camelot Info
Cartes Carlton
Coles
Le Rouet
Pot Pourri
Reminiscence

Musique, électronique, photo

Alliance Web-Commerce
Astral Photo Images
Aurum Software
Mallette Informatique
Megaweb Internet Network
Radio Shack
Roland Therien
Ultimate Technographics

Coiffure - cosmétiques

Body Shop
Coiffure et Esthétique Jaques
Despars
Dans Un Jardin
Fragrance

Spécialités

Cellular Solution
Entretien Precal
Gravel Saturn Saab Isuzu
Primus Canada
Rogers A T & T
SAQ - Sociéte des Alcools du Québec
Scali Accessoires
Star Data Systems Inc.
X-Presse

Alimentation

La Charcuterie de Bon Goût
Laura Secord
Mmmuffins

Restaurants

AL Van Houtte
Café Dépôt
Café Tarantino
Dunkin' Donuts
Fontaine Santé
Franx Suprême
Giorgio Express
Gourmet Med
Katz Deli à l'Ancienne
Marchelino
Poulet Frit Kentucky
Restaurant A&W
Restaurant Caravelle
Restaurant Club Lounge 737
Restaurant Marché Movenpick
Restaurant Mr Ma
Restaurant Tiki Ming
Salades Belles Saisons
Subway Sous-Marins & Salades
Sukiyaki
Valentino's

Divertissement

L'Ambassadeur Théâtre

Petit déjeuner

Restauration à Montréal

Québécois

Salle à manger Gérard-Delage (Hôtel de l'Institut)
3535, rue Saint-Denis
Montréal, Qc H2X 3P1
Métro: Sherbrooke
Tél.: (514) 282-5161 **Télécopieur:** (514) 873-9893
Sans frais: 1 800 361-5111
Site Internet: www.ithq.qc.ca
Courriel: conciergerie@ithq.qc.ca

Cuisine gastonomique continentale avec fins produits québécois.

Horaire: tous les jours, 7h30 à 10h, midi à 13h30, 18h à 20h30
Personnes handicapées: accès total
Prix moyen: plus de 25$
Cartes de crédit: American Express, Carte Blanche/Diners Club, Interac, MasterCard, Visa

Français

Pierre du Calvet a.d. 1725 Hostellerie
405, rue Bonsecours
Montréal, Qc H2Y 3C3
Métro: Champ-de-Mars
Tél.: (514) 282-1725 **Télécopieur:** (514) 282-0456
Site Internet: www.pierreducalvet.ca

Fine cuisine française classique. Ambiance romantique.

Horaire: tous les jours, 17h à 23h
Personnes handicapées: accès partiel
Prix moyen: plus de 25$
Cartes de crédit: American Express, Carte Blanche/Diners Club, enRoute, MasterCard, Visa

Végétarien

Le Commensal (McGill)
1204, avenue McGill College
Montréal, Qc H3B 4J8
Métro: McGill
Tél.: (514) 871-1480
Télécopieur: (514) 871-0016

Buffet libre-service, chaud, froid et desserts. Payez en fonction du poids.

Horaire: tous les jours, 11h à 22h
Personnes handicapées: accès total
Prix moyen: moins de 15$
Cartes de crédit: American Express, enRoute/Diners Club, Interac, MasterCard, Visa

Indien

Restaurant Le Taj
2077, rue Stanley
Montréal, Qc H3A 1R7
Métro: Peel
Tél.: (514) 845-9015
Télécopieur: (514) 845-8348

Cuisine tandoori et végétarienne. Grillades. Boutique où l'on retrouve des artefacts indiens.

Horaire: lundi au jeudi, 11h à 14h30, 17h à 22h30; vendredi et samedi 11h30 à 14h30, 17h à 23h; dimanche, midi à 14h30, 17h à 22h30
Personnes handicapées: accès total
Prix moyen: 15$ à 25$
Cartes de crédit: American Express, Carte Blanche/Diners Club, enRoute, MasterCard, Visa

Programmation de "Jazz à l'année"

The New Montreal Jazz Collective

Dimanche 30 septembre, 20 h, Spectrum de Montréal
(Gratuit – dans le cadre des Journées de la culture)

Lors du plus récent Festival de Jazz, on annonçait le concert du New Montreal Jazz Collective comme étant un concert unique. Mais le succès remporté par les huit membres de cette brillante relève du jazz montréalais fut tel qu'ils récidivent! Cette réunion de musiciens tous plus talentueux les uns que les autres promet certes d'autres moments magiques… à la demande générale. Avec Thüryn Von Pranke (piano), Christine Jensen (saxophone), Yannick Rieu (saxophone), Kelsley Grant (trombone), Maxime St-Pierre (trompette), Fraser Hollins (contrebasse) et Martin Auguste (batterie).

Nils Petter Molvaer

Mercredi 3 octobre, 20 h, Cabaret du Capitole de Québec (24,50 $, avant taxes et frais de service)

Le public pourra enfin assister au concert du trompettiste scandinave. Il nous propose une musique improvisée qui s'alimente de plusieurs nouveaux courants comme le drum'n'bass, l'ambiant et le jungle, mais en continuant de puiser dans le rock et le jazz, ses deux réelles sources d'inspiration. Pour décrire son travail plusieurs ont d'ailleurs parlé de filiation avec le disque "Bitches Brew" de Miles Davis. Le créateur cite lui-même Don Cherry et Jon Hassell parmi ses influences. En première partie: Rodes'n Rythms, avec DJ Pocket et le claviériste Denis Raoul Hébert. Un concert très attendu!

The Robert Cray Band

Jeudi 1er novembre, 20 h, Spectrum de Montréal (28,50 $ plus taxes et frais de service)

Le guitariste, compositeur et interprète de renommée internationale Robert Cray n'avait pas présenté de concert dans la métropole depuis quelques années. Voilà donc une belle occasion de revoir ou de découvrir sur scène ce prodigieux musicien, lequel s'arrêtera en sol montréalais pour nous présenter ses nouvelles chansons issues de "Shoulda Been Home," son plus récent album. Un blues de facture plutôt classique qui ensorcelle! La première partie du spectacle sera entre les mains (et la voix!) du percutant guitariste et harmoniciste d'origine canadienne Ray Bonneville. Le blues à son meilleur!

Kelly Joe Phelps

Vendredi 23 novembre, 20 h, Spectrum de Montréal (15,50 $ plus taxes et frais de service)

Musique folk saupoudrée de blues, de jazz et de country gospel. Difficile de traduire en quelques mots la musique que nous offre Kelly Joe Phelps… et tout aussi difficile de lui résister! Après avoir vu son second album, "Shine Eyes Mister Zen," se faire dorloter par la critique et mériter le titre d'album blues acoustique de l'année par le magazine Blues Revue, le magnifique guitariste et chanteur revient à Montréal, cette fois pour présenter les pièces de son nouvel album, "Sky Like a Broken Clock," sur lequel il poursuit de plus belle ce brillant amalgame de blues et de rythmes du jazz dont il connaît si bien la recette.

François Carrier Trio

Invité spécial: Uri Caine
22, 23 et 24 novembre, 20 h, Théâtre La Chapelle (20,00 $ plus taxes et frais de service)

C'est en fondant sa propre formation, sous le nom de Trio François Carrier, que le populaire saxophoniste québécois s'est d'abord fait connaître. En 1999, le leader de la formation réunissait le contrebassiste Pierre Côté, le batteur Michel Lambert et le pianiste Steve Amirault pour l'enregistrement du "DC Compassion," gagnant du Juno "Meilleur album jazz de l'année." Avec comme invité spécial le pianiste établi à New York Uri Caine la formation revient nous induire de ses audaces. Un réel événement à vivre, dans l'intimité du Théâtre La Chapelle!

Professions et métiers II

CURRICULUM VITAE

Nom:

Prénoms:

Adresse:

Numéro de téléphone:

Date de naissance:

Lieu de naissance:

Nationalité:

FORMATION

Établissements scolaires:

Diplômes:

Clubs et activités parascolaires:

EXPÉRIENCE PROFESSIONNELLE

AUTRES RENSEIGNEMENTS

Isabelle Adjani

Adjani, Isabelle (1955-), actrice française qui, après avoir débuté très jeune à la Comédie-Française, s'est principalement consacrée au cinéma. Son jeu enflammé et extrêmement expressif, mais aussi son aisance légère ont contribué à l'imposer comme l'une des comédiennes et actrices les plus douées de sa génération.

Née d'un père algérien et d'une mère allemande, Isabelle Adjani fait ses débuts au cinéma, à l'âge de quatorze ans, dans *le Petit Bougnat* de Bernard Toublanc-Michel, puis entre en 1973 à la Comédie-Française. Elle y incarne notamment Agnès dans *l'École des femmes* de Molière, le rôle-titre d'*Ondine* de Jean Giraudoux et joue dans *Port-Royal* d'Henry de Montherlant (1974). Au cours de cette période, Isabelle Adjani apparaît au cinéma dans *Faustine ou le Bel Été* de Nina Companeez (1971) et dans *la Gifle* de Claude Pinoteau (1974), son premier grand rôle. Choisie par François Truffaut pour interpréter le rôle principal dans *l'Histoire d'Adèle H.* (1975), celui d'Adèle Hugo, poursuivant jusqu'au désespoir un amant indifférent, elle quitte alors la Comédie-Française.

Par la suite, elle est tour à tour l'interprète de Roman Polanski dans *le Locataire* (1976), d'André Téchiné dans *Barocco* (1976) et de Werner Herzog dans *Nosferatu, fantôme de la* nuit (1979). Belle et fragile, elle incarne une héroïne romantique dans le film d'André Téchiné, *les Sœurs Brontë* (1979), et reçoit le prix d'interprétation féminine au festival de Cannes (1981) pour la subtilité psychologique de son jeu dans *Possession* d'Andrzej Zulawski (1981). L'année suivante, elle s'illustre dans *Tout feu, tout flamme* de Jean-Paul Rappeneau, *Antonietta* de Carlos Saura et *Mortelle randonnée* de Claude Miller, film dans lequel elle incarne un personnage d'un type nouveau: celui d'une femme froide et énigmatique. Son interprétation dans *l'Été meurtrier* de Jean Becker (1983) lui vaut un césar en 1984. L'année suivante, elle apparaît aux côtés de Christophe Lambert et de Jean-Hughes Anglade dans *Subway*, réalisé par Luc Besson, qui connaît un grand succès public. *Camille Claudel*, réalisé par Bruno Nuytten en 1988, marque un des temps forts de sa carrière; elle y incarne un personnage tourmenté aux frontières de la folie. En 1994, Patrice Chéreau fait d'elle une *Reine Margot* saluée par l'ensemble de la critique.

En octobre 2000, Isabelle Adjani s'arrache d'une longue retraite et revient sur les planches pour interpréter au théâtre Marigny-Robert Hossein le rôle de Marguerite Gautier dans *la Dame aux camélias* de René de Ceccaty, d'après l'œuvre d'Alexandre Dumas fils, dans une mise en scène d'Alfredo Arias: elle s'y révèle à la fois d'une beauté mûrie et quasi impériale et d'une assurance apaisée.

Jeanne d'Arc

Ô Jeanne, sans sépulcre et sans portrait,
toi qui savais que le tombeau des héros
est le cœur des vivants...

André Malraux
Inscription figurant sur le monument national à Jeanne d'Arc

Capturée près de Compiègne, Jeanne d'Arc est emmenée à Rouen à **Noël 1430** pour être jugée.

Elle fut internée dans la forteresse du XIIIe siècle, dans la tour dite plus tard "Tour de la Pucelle", dont quelques vestiges subsistent - 102, rue Jeanne d'Arc. ❶

Bien qu'inculpée d'hérésie par un tribunal religieux, elle fut placée dans une prison laïque et gardée par des geôliers anglais et non par des femmes. Dans le donjon - "Tour Jeanne d'Arc" ❷ - elle n'y entrera qu'une seule fois pour y subir la torture à laquelle les juges renonceront devant son attitude.

Le procès commença le **9 février 1431** ; les interrogatoires, conduits par l'évêque de Beauvais - Cauchon - eurent lieu dans l'enceinte de la forteresse et non pas à l'Officialité de l'Archevêché. Les 70 articles du réquisitoire furent récusés par Jeanne ; seul, un condensé de 12 articles fut soumis aux théologiens et docteurs qui la condamnèrent comme hérétique, blasphématrice, schismatique.

Le **24 mai 1431**, Jeanne fut amenée au cimetière Saint-Ouen ❸ pour la séance publique de l'abjuration. Cauchon usa encore d'une supercherie ; le texte signé par Jeanne d'une croix ne lui fut lu que partiellement.

De retour dans sa prison, Jeanne ne trouva pour s'habiller que des habits d'homme, ce qui permit à Cauchon, le **28 mai**, d'ouvrir "le procès de relapse". Les juges rendirent la sentence de condamnation au bûcher dans l'Officialité ❹.

Le **30 mai 1431**, sur la place du Vieux-Marché ❺, Jeanne fut brûlée vive, devant les autorités anglaises, les représentants de l'Eglise et une foule nombreuse. Dite hérétique et excommuniée, elle reçut néanmoins l'Eucharistie avant son supplice. Sur l 'échafaud, elle demanda une croix qui lui fut présentée.

Cauchon n'obtiendra pas la renonciation qu'il escomptait.

Quand tout fut fini, le bourreau alla jeter les cendres de Jeanne, ainsi que son cœur qui n'avait pas brûlé, dans la Seine, à l'entrée du pont ❻, car aucune relique ne devait être conservée.

En **1455**, la mère de Jeanne, Isabelle Romée, obtenait du pape l'autorisation de demander la révision du procès. Le **7 juillet 1456**, la séance solennelle de réhabilitation eut lieu au cimetière Saint-Ouen ❸, le procès ayant été conduit dans l'Archevêché ❹. Il était stipulé que la ville de Rouen devrait édifier une croix à l'emplacement du supplice ❺.
Jeanne ne devait être béatifiée qu'en 1909, et canonisée en 1920.

Rouen

événements

Une ville de fêtes

Rouen vous donne rendez-vous...

Janvier	Salon des artistes indépendants (Halle aux Toiles) Puces Rouennaises d'hiver (Parc des Expositions)
Mars	Festival du Cinéma Nordique
Mars à octobre	Les Heures Musicales de Saint-Maclou (Eglise Saint-Maclou)
Avril	Foire Internationale de Rouen (Parc des Expositions) Suivez le guide
Mai	24 Heures motonautiques Internationales Grand Prix de Danse sportive Voix de Fêtes / Fêtes de Rouen / Fêtes Jeanne d'Arc
Juin	Fête de la Musique
Juin/juillet	Semaine Européenne des Orgues
Septembre	Marché Rétrophoto Puces Rouennaises d'automne "Ecoute s'il pleut" / Festival de Jazz
Octobre	Festival Octobre en Normandie
Octobre/nov.	Fête foraine : Foire Saint-Romain (Quais bas rive sud)
Décembre	Festival du livre de jeunesse Marché de Noël

Les marchés

- **Place Saint-Marc (E3) :** les mardi, vendredi et samedi de 8h à 18h30; le dimanche de 8h à 13h30 (brocante).
- **Place du Vieux-Marché (C2) :** les mardi, mercredi, jeudi, vendredi, samedi et dimanche de 6h à 13h30.
- **Place des Emmurées (C5) :** les mardi, jeudi (brocante) et samedi de 8h à 18h30.

L'imparfait

Pour former l'imparfait:

- prends la forme **nous** du présent: **(nous) passons**
- enlève la terminaison **–ons: pass**
- ajoute ces terminaisons:

(je)	**–ais**
(tu)	**–ais**
(il/elle/on)	**–ait**
(nous)	**–ions**
(vous)	**–iez**
(ils/elles)	**–aient**

Par exemple:

passer	**finir**	**perdre**
(nous pass/ons)	(nous finiss/ons)	(nous perd/ons)
Je passais	**Je finissais**	**Je perdais**
Tu passais	**Tu finissais**	**Tu perdais**
Il/Elle/On passait	**Il/Elle/On finissait**	**Il/Elle/On perdait**
Nous passions	**Nous finissions**	**Nous perdions**
Vous passiez	**Vous finissiez**	**Vous perdiez**
Ils/Elles passaient	**Ils/Elles finissaient**	**Ils/Elles perdaient**

Tous les verbes ont les mêmes terminaisons à l'imparfait.

Seul le verbe **être** est irrégulier à l'imparfait:

J'étais	**Nous étions**
Tu étais	**Vous étiez**
Il/Elle/On était	**Ils/Elles étaient**

Voici quelques expressions utiles:

C'était (super).
Il faisait (beau).
Il y avait (beaucoup de monde).

N'*oublie pas*! L'*imparfait s'emploie*:

• pour décrire les choses/ les gens au passé – **Quand j'étais petit, j'avais les cheveux très courts.**	• pour parler d'activités habituelles au passé – **On allait toujours au bord de la mer.**	• pour parler de ce qui se passait au moment d'un événement – **Je regardais la télé quand le téléphone a sonné.**

François Truffaut

Truffaut, François (1932-1984), réalisateur et critique de cinéma français, l'un des chefs de file de la Nouvelle Vague.

Né à Paris, François Truffaut quitte l'école à l'âge de quatorze ans après une enfance malheureuse. Emprisonné pour désertion, il commence sa carrière comme critique dans les *Cahiers du cinéma*, la revue fondée par André Bazin. À la fin des années cinquante, il réalise ses premiers films en tant qu'auteur ou co-auteur. Son premier long métrage, *les Quatre Cents Coups* (1959), fait l'effet d'une bombe. Il y relate l'histoire d'Antoine Doinel, un adolescent incompris incarné par Jean-Pierre Léaud. Ce personnage, pour lequel François Truffaut s'est en partie inspiré de sa propre histoire, est repris par la suite dans une série de films tendrement humoristiques : *Baisers volés* (1968), *Domicile conjugal* (1970) et *l'Amour en fuite* (1979).

Les films de François Truffaut mêlent le comique, l'émotion, le suspense (il est un fervent admirateur d'Alfred Hitchcock) et le mélodrame : *Tirez sur le pianiste* (1960) mélange avec habileté moments de gaieté et scènes de suspense, *Jules et Jim* (1962) décrit l'histoire d'un couple à trois, *l'Histoire d'Adèle H* (1975) et *la Chambre verte* (1978), au style visuel très évocateur, mettent en scène d'une part, des amours impossibles et d'autre part, le culte des morts. En hommage au cinéma, François Truffaut réalise *la Nuit américaine* (1973), qui remporte l'oscar du meilleur film étranger aux États-Unis.

Le Dernier Métro (1980), évocation de la relation amoureuse entre une directrice de théâtre mariée, incarnée par Catherine Deneuve, et un jeune comédien (Gérard Depardieu), sous l'Occupation à Paris, place le thème de la vérité au cœur d'une mise en abyme du jeu d'acteurs et de la représentation artistique, qu'elle soit cinématographique ou théâtrale. Le film est le plus important succès public jamais rencontré par François Truffaut. *Vivement dimanche* (1983) constitue sa dernière œuvre, interprétée notamment par Fanny Ardant et Jean-Louis Trintignant.

Les Invalides

INVALIDES
TOMBEAU DE NAPOLEON
SAINT-LOUIS DES INVALIDES
MUSEE DE L'ARMEE

Monument - Eglise - Musée

C'est à partir de 1677, sous la direction de l'architecte Jules Hardouin-Mansart, que fut édifiée l'église du Dôme dont le lanternon ajouré culmine à 107 m. Les funérailles nationales qui ont accompagné le transfert des cendres de Napoléon I ont été célébrées le 15 décembre 1840. L'édification du tombeau commandée au sculpteur Visconti s'est achevée en 1861, date à laquelle y furent inhumés les restes de l'Empereur. Le Musée de l'Armée est le plus important au monde. Il couvre l'histoire de la France jusqu'à la deuxième guerre mondiale.

Adjectives

Serge
Thomas
Mme Dupont
Didier
Un coca, s'il vous plaît.
Sylvie
Et puis....
Hi, hi, hi!

Carnet intime de Patricia Kaas

Signe zodiacal: Sagittaire
Surnoms: "Pat" pour les intimes, "Patty" pour la famille, et "Patronne" en tournée
Plat favori: Escalope panée, frites
Péché mignon: Les petits dominos en chocolat fourrés de pain d'épices qu'on achète sur les marchés de Noël
Livre préféré: *Amok* de Stefan Sweig
Film préféré: *Autant en emporte le vent*
Parfum: Aromatics Elixir de Clinique
Type d'homme: Clark Gable, les hommes aux cheveux gominés, comme son père Joseph

Elle aime...
La famille
L'enfance
Noël et la neige
Prendre un bon bain
Les ambiances bougies
Les fleurs

Elle n'aime pas...
Le caviar
La souffrance
Les mensonges
Les coups de soleil
Les desserts trop sucrés
Être stressée

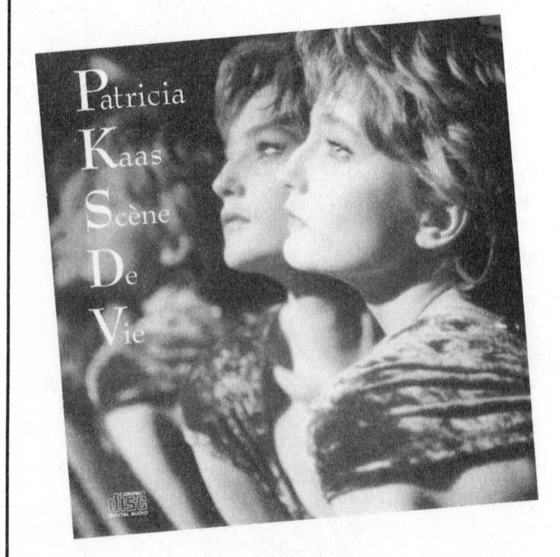

Discographie
Mademoiselle chante, 1988
Scène de vie, 1990
Carnets de scène, 1991
Je te dis vous, 1993
Tour de charme, 1994
Dans ma chair, 1997
Rendez-vous, 1998
Le mot de passe, 1999
Ce sera nous, 2000
Les indispensables, 2001
Rien ne s'arrête, 2001
Piano Bar, 2002
Sexe fort, 2004
Toute la musique..., 2005

Le monde francophone

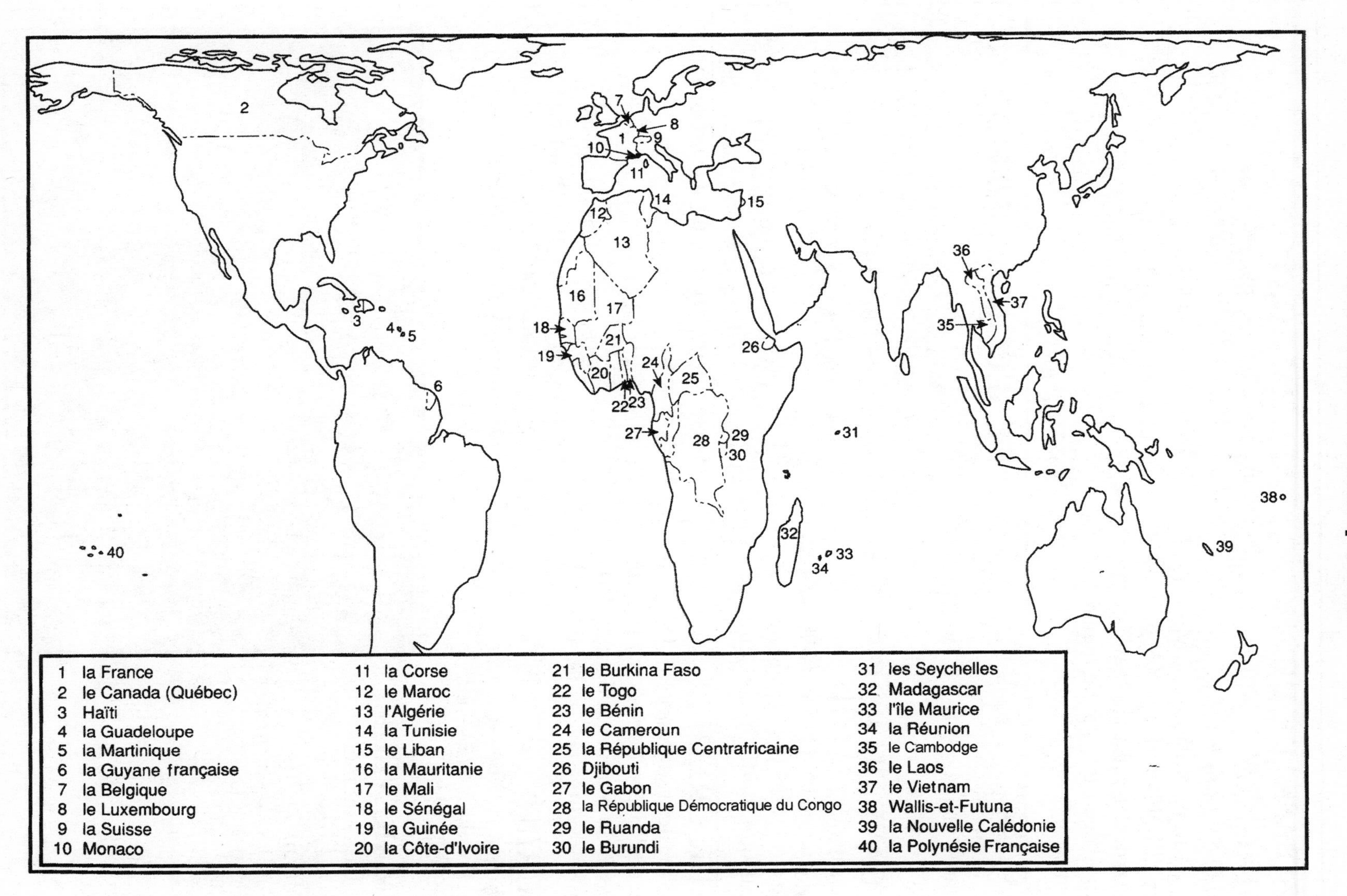

Restaurants à Fort-de-France

"L'AMBASSADE DE BRETAGNE"
spécialités bretonnes
Zone piétonne. Village de Rivière Roche (entrée ZI Jambette). Tél: 0596.50.24.50.
Ouvert tous les midi sauf sam. et dim.
Jeudi arrivage de fruits de mer de Bretagne.

"LA CASE"
créole, français, italien
108, rue E. Deproge. Tél: 0596.63.04.00 sauf dim.

"LA CAVE DU ROI"
crêpes, salades
4, rue Garnier Pagès. Tél: 0596.60.22.63.
Tous les jours de 12h à 15h et de 19h à 24h sauf sam. midi, dim. et lun.

"CŒUR CRÉOLE"
cuisine locale traditionnelle
Village de Rivière Roche, rue Piétonne (au-dessus du Manikou Nights). Fermé sam. midi et dim. Tél: 0596.50.60.66.

"L'ÉCRIN"
spécialités africaines et créoles
17, rue Franklin Roosevelt.
Tél: 0596.63.12.37.

"LE MAREYEUR"
créole, fruits de mer
Pte des Nègres.
Tél: 0596.61.74.70.

"LE PAPAGAYO"
français, italien, glacier
Rond Pt de Didier. Tél: 0596.72.62.62.
Sauf dim. midi et lun. soir.

"LE RAMSIS"
spécialités orientales, libanaises, pizzas et pâtes
123, rue Blénac. Tél: 0596.70.47.78.

"LE SECOND SOUFFLE"
végétarien
27, rue Blénac. Tél: 0596.63.44.11.
73, rue Albert Camus. Tél: 0596.57.14.28.
Le midi sauf sam., dim.

"LAS TAPAS DE SEVILLA"
espagnol
7, rue Garnier Pagès. Tél: 0596.63.71.23.
Ouvert du lun. au sam. soir jusqu'à 23h en semaine et 24h le sam. Fermé le sam. midi et le dim.

"LE ZÉNITH"
18, bd Allègre. Tél: 0596.60.35.59.
Ouvert ts les jrs de 18h à 1h du matin.
Le vend. et sam. de 18h à 3h du matin.
Fermé dim. et lun. soir. Pizzas livrées à domicile.

Recette martiniquaise

Acras de morue

Ingrédients:

200 g de morue séchée et salée
1 oignon
3 cives
3 gousses d'ail
1 pointe de piment
2 branches de persil hachées
300 g de farine
1 sachet de levure
1 œuf entier
$1/2$ C. à C. de bicarbonate de soude
sel, poivre, huile

Faire pocher la morue dans deux eaux successives, puis chiquetailler en prenant soin d'enlever la peau et les arrêtes. Hacher l'ensemble des épices. Tamiser la farine dans un saladier, incorporer la morue émiettée, l'oignon, l'ail et les cives hachés. Ajouter le persil et la pointe de piment. Mélanger l'ensemble en incorporant la levure, le bicarbonate de soude et l'œuf entier. Saler légèrement, poivrer et verser de l'eau jusqu'à l'obtention d'une pâte très homogène. Laisser reposer la pâte quelques heures avant de confectionner les acras en faisant frire des petites cuillères à café de pâte dans un bain d'huile.

Témoignages de Tahiti

1. Lune de miel

Charles et Béatrice, 28 ans, Sète

Nous nous sommes mariés en juin dernier et avons décidé de partir en lune de miel à Tahiti en juillet. Ce voyage de noces a été une véritable réussite. De toute façon, quel plus beau cadeau de mariage qu'un tel séjour au bout du monde? Nos parents et nos amis nous ont vraiment gâtés. Si Tahiti, Moorea et Manihi nous ont beaucoup plus, nous avons préféré Bora Bora et Huahine dont nous gardons un merveilleux souvenir. À Bora Bora, nous occupions un superbe bungalow sur pilotis où nous pouvions contempler ce lagon mythique et admirer les centaines de poissons multicolores qui passaient sous notre chambre grâce à une table en verre. Chaque matin nous commandions un délicieux petit déjeuner qui nous était apporté en pirogue à balancier par une vahiné. Mais surtout, nous sommes tombés sous le charme de Huahine qui nous est apparue plus authentique. À Huahine, belle, sauvage et préservée, nous avons vraiment eu le sentiment d'appartenir à ce monde polynésien si attachant et si accueillant.

2. Voyage pas cher

Jean-Jacques, 24 ans, Aix-en-Provence

La Polynésie, j'en rêvais depuis longtemps mais je pensais que je ne pourrais jamais y aller à cause du prix du billet. Tenté par la destination, j'ai quand même décidé d'aller voir à Paris la Maison de Tahiti où une polynésienne m'a organisé un séjour bon marché. En fait, je suis parti au mois de mai et j'ai pu voir trois îles, Tahiti, Moorea et Raiatea grâce au pass Air Tahiti, la compagnie locale, et aux petits prix proposés dans les pensions de famille qui m'avaient été conseillées. Pour la bouffe, j'allais sur les marchés et je mangeais "à la locale" principalement du poisson cru que j'achetais pour pas grand chose. Mon budget n'a pas explosé et avec mon amie on est bien décidé à repartir dans deux ans.

3. Croisières

Huguette et René, 66 ans, retraités, Alençon

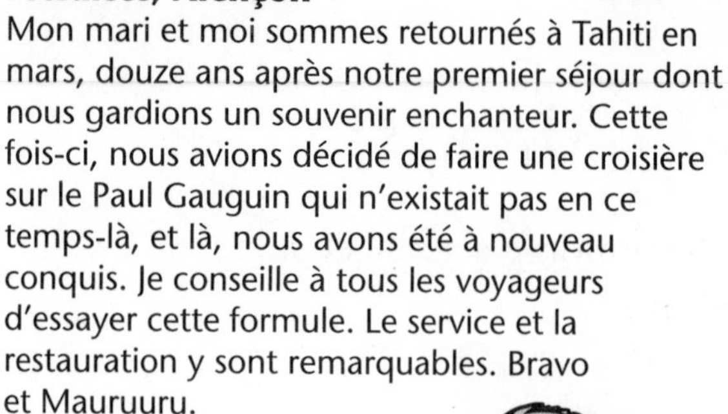

Mon mari et moi sommes retournés à Tahiti en mars, douze ans après notre premier séjour dont nous gardions un souvenir enchanteur. Cette fois-ci, nous avions décidé de faire une croisière sur le Paul Gauguin qui n'existait pas en ce temps-là, et là, nous avons été à nouveau conquis. Je conseille à tous les voyageurs d'essayer cette formule. Le service et la restauration y sont remarquables. Bravo et Mauruuru.

4. Le lagon

Christine, 32 ans, Lisieux

Passionnée depuis toujours par la mer et particulièrement la faune marine, je vous écris pour vous dire combien les scènes aquatiques auxquelles j'ai assisté dans les lagons de Rangiroa et Bora Bora sont sublimes. J'ai eu un coup de cœur pour vos si beaux lagons. Je n'ai jamais vu autant de poissons, aux couleurs si vives, dans aussi peu d'eau. Imaginez qu'à un mètre de profondeur seulement, je pouvais déjà contempler ces ballets extraordinaires. En plongeant plus profond, j'ai été fasciné par la grâce des raies manta qui sont loin d'être sauvages et évoluent autour de vous sans peur. Tout comme les petits requins, si vifs, mais fort heureusement inoffensifs.

5. Tourisme vert

Samuel, 48 ans, Quimper

À Tahiti, j'avais envie de gravir les montagnes, leurs flancs verdoyants et leurs sommets dont certains paraissent inaccessibles. Tout un monde à découvrir. Je me suis enfoncé avec délice dans les profondes vallées noyées de verdure tropicale. Je me suis même pris pour Robinson ou pour un découvreur tellement j'avais le sentiment d'être seul sur ces îles. C'est dommage qu'on ne pense pas systématiquement à faire de la randonnée à Tahiti. Mais je vous assure que vous découvrirez, en toute sécurité, un paysage de verdure et de nature étonnant. Et c'est pareil aux Marquises et à Huahine.

Présentation générale de la Guyane française

Situation

La Guyane française est située dans le nord-est de l'Amérique du Sud, entre le Surinam et le Brésil. C'est le plus vaste et le plus forestier des départements français: 94% de son territoire sont recouverts par la forêt équitoriale.

Climat

Le climat de la Guyane est équatorial avec un taux d'hydrométrie d'environ 90%. La moyenne des températures est de 27°C.

Population

Lors du recensement de 1990, la population de la Guyane était de 114 678 habitants.
La population de Guyane est caractérisée par sa grande diversité:
Les **Créoles guyanais** (environ 40% de la population)
Les **Amérindiens** (4 500 personnes)
Les **Noirs-marrons** (4 000 personnes)
Les **H'mongs**, arrivés en 1977, représentent environ 2 000 personnes regroupées sur les communes de Cacao et Javouhey.
Les **Métropolitains** représentent actuellement environ 12% de la population.
Les autres populations (Chinois, Libanais, Brésiliens, Haïtiens, Surinamiens) représentent près de 40% de la population de Guyane.

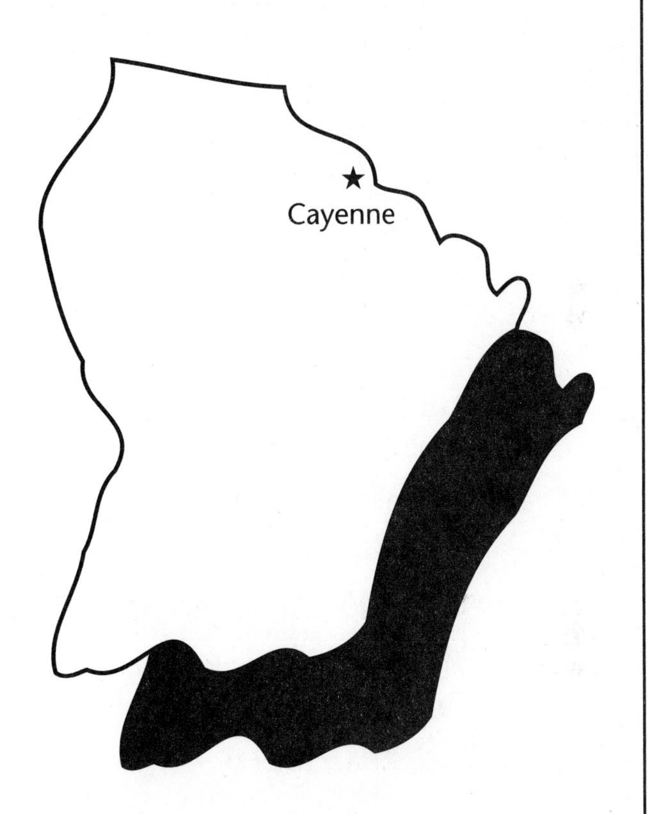

Département français

La Guyane est un département français depuis la loi du 19 mars 1946. Elle comprend deux arrondissements, 22 communes et 19 cantons. Elle est représentée au Parlement par deux députés et un sénateur, et par un conseiller au Conseil Économique et Social. Département français d'outre-mer, la Guyane fait partie de l'Union Européenne, et bénéficie des mesures spécifiques qui adaptent le droit communautaire à la situation du département.

MadagasCartes

D'abord, faites des recherches sur Madagascar en ligne. Puis envoyez une carte postale virtuelle à un(e) ami(e). Suivez ces instructions:

1. Allez à ce site sur Internet: http://cartes.malango.net/cartes-madagascar-0.htm
2. Choisissez d'abord une photo de Madagascar que vous aimez.
3. Remplissez le nom et l'adresse e-mail du destinaire.
4. Remplissez votre nom et votre adresse e-mail.
5. Écrivez votre message.
   - Écrivez la date.
   - Saluez votre ami(e).
   - Dites ce que vous avez fait à Madagascar.
   - Dites pourquoi vous aimez Madagascar.
   - Donnez deux faits sur Madagascar de votre lecture (*reading*).
   - Dites "Grosses bises" et signez votre nom.
6. Cliquez pour envoyer la carte postale.

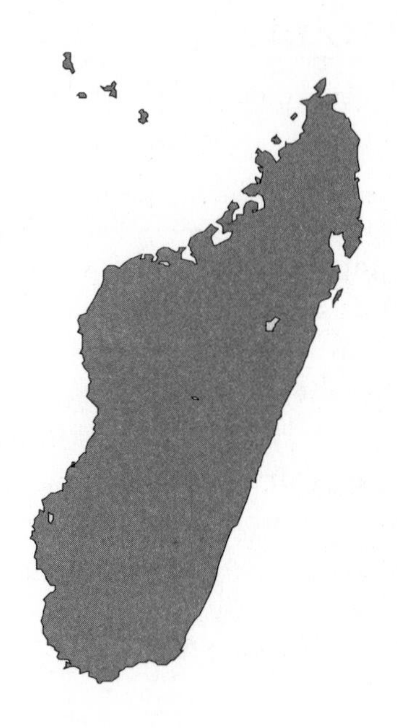

Culture sénégalaise

Chaque pays a ses règles de conduite, ses formules de politesse, ses usages, souvent très éloignés des siens. Pour ne pas faire de faux pas au Sénégal, lisez ce petit mémo.

Salutations

Les salutations sont extrêmement importantes. Ici on dit «Bonjour» tout le temps à tout le monde, même à quelqu'un qu'on n'a jamais vu et qu'on ne reverra jamais. Le «Salameleikum» (réponse: «Aleikum Salam») est de bon ton.

Tenue

Montrer ses jambes (surtout pour les filles, mais aussi pour les garçons) est très mal vu par les musulmans. Évitez donc les shorts et mini-jupes.

Repas

Le repas se prend accroupi par terre ou assis sur un petit tabouret, dans un plat commun, souvent avec la main. Déchaussez-vous avant de marcher sur la natte, lavez-vous les mains et n'utilisez que la main droite en mangeant. On boit seulement après avoir fini le plat principal.

Thé

La cérémonie du thé est très importante. Si vous acceptez la première tasse, il vous faudra aller jusqu'à la troisième, la plus sucrée.

Marchandage

L'objectif premier du marchandage n'est pas de faire baisser les prix. Il s'agit avant tout d'un échange. Prenez votre temps, parlez d'autre chose, exchamez-vous bien fort. Plus longue sera la discussion, plus vous aurez l'estime de votre interlocuteur.

Superstition

Acheter du charbon de bois, du sel, du poivre, du piment, des aiguilles, des lames de rasoir après la tombée de la nuit risque d'attirer les mauvais esprits.

Prières

L'Islam impose cinq prières quotidiennes, à des heures bien précises, faites après des ablutions rituelles. Ne vous étonnez donc pas de voir certaines personnes se laver les pieds, la tête et les mains sur le bord du troittoir, ou votre boutiquier abandonner ses clients sans préavis pour prier derrière le comptoir. Patientez; tout ça est très naturel.

Mendicité

Vous serez sans doute surpris de rencontrer beaucoup de mendiants, dont des personnes handicapées par la polio ou la lèpre. Donnez une petite pièce si vous le pouvez, et surtout un grand sourire. Faire l'aumône au moins une fois par jour est une recommandation de l'Islam. Quand on a déjà donné l'aumône à un premier mendiant, on peut dire à tout autre: «Egg na» qui signifie «C'est arrivé.»

Île de Gorée

Un quart d'heure seulement en chaloupe suffit pour relier Gorée au reste du continent. D'une superficie de 28 hectares, cette île exerce un charme et une fascination extraordinaires sur les visiteurs qui ressentent une émotion particulière en déambulant dans ses ruelles étroites et paisibles.

Trois siècles durant, de nombreux africains ont été réduits à l'esclavage et embarqués, à partir de l'île de Gorée en direction du continent américain. La célèbre Maison des esclaves, un des musées les plus visités au Sénégal, conserve encore toute la poignante réalité de ce pan de l'histoire universelle.

Tour à tour occupée par les Portugais, les Hollandais, les Français, les Anglais qui la rendirent à la France en 1817, Gorée était une escale obligée pour les navires européens à destination de l'Amérique et de l'Asie. Dès l'abolition de l'esclavage en 1848, le déclin de l'île est inévitable, surtout avec la création de Dakar en 1857 et Rufisque en 1859. A partir de 1929, Gorée est annexée à la capitale.

Aujourd'hui, l'île abrite de nombreuses résidences secondaires et accueille tous les jours de nombreux visiteurs. Plusieurs sites sont dignes d'intérêt : le musée historique, dans le fort d'Estrées, où l'histoire du Sénégal est passée en revue, de la préhistoire à l'indépendance, en passant par la période coloniale, le musée de la femme qui présente des vitrines très originales sur le rôle des femmes sénégalaises dans les sociétés traditionnelles et modernes et le musée de la mer, célèbre pour ses collections de poissons et mollusques marins.

Le Castel, plateau rocheux recouvert de fortifications, domine l'île et offre une vue superbe sur Dakar. En face du marché, se dresse le Relais de l'Espadon, ancienne résidence du gouverneur français de Gorée transformée en hôtel et aujourd'hui abandonné.

Fêtes en Côte-d'Ivoire

La fête des ignames

L'igname, originaire du Ghana, fut introduite en Côte-d'Ivoire par le peuple Akan, lors de leur migration dans notre pays. C'est pendant la traversée de la grande forêt que le précieux légume leur fut le plus utile pour lutter contre la famine.

L'igname est fêtée aujourd'hui au mois de février par les 11 tribus Akan, pour célébrer la fin de l'année et le début de la nouvelle année. Ce jour-là, le Roi, paré d'or, entame une procession au cours de laquelle les symboles du pouvoir royal s'exécutent à la danse "Kinian-pli."

Après une douche purificatrice, des sacrifices sont exécutés. Une partie des offrandes sera brûlée tandis que l'autre sera partagée entre les différents participants comme symbole de l'union des morts et des vivants.

Le Dipri

Venu de Gomon, le Dipri est la commémoration du sacrifice de Bidyo, fils d'un paysan touché par la famine, qui sur les conseils d'un génie a découpé son fils en morceau avant de l'enterrer; mais qu'elle ne fut pas sa surprise de découvrir au matin qu'un champ d'igname avait poussé à l'endroit même où il avait enterré son fils.

Depuis, chaque année à la fin du mois d'avril, les Angré Kpone ou mangeurs d'âme se réunissent autour du lac pour faire des incantations magiques, en vue d'éloigner le mauvais sort du village. Les femmes se réunissent nues dans le village pour neutraliser les maléfices et accomplir le rite du Sokroyibé. Quand elles ont terminé, le village peu à peu revit, et tout le monde peut sortir de sa maison. Toute la journée, le bien et le mal vont s'affronter; au coucher du soleil, le mal est vaincu et les Abidji peuvent se purifier dans le lac Kporon.

L'Abissa

Coutume bassamoise, la fête de l'Abissa se déroule au mois de novembre pendant une semaine.

À l'origine un ancêtre avait découvert en pleine brousse des morts et a exécuté à ce moment-là une danse macabre. De retour au village, l'homme fit instituer cette danse en hommage aux morts. Dès lors le grand tam-tam "Edougbele" sort lors de la grande fête pour rythmer la fanfare, dans le quartier France. Le septième jour, on raccompagne le tam-tam en émettant des vœux et la fête se poursuit en un grand bal costumé.

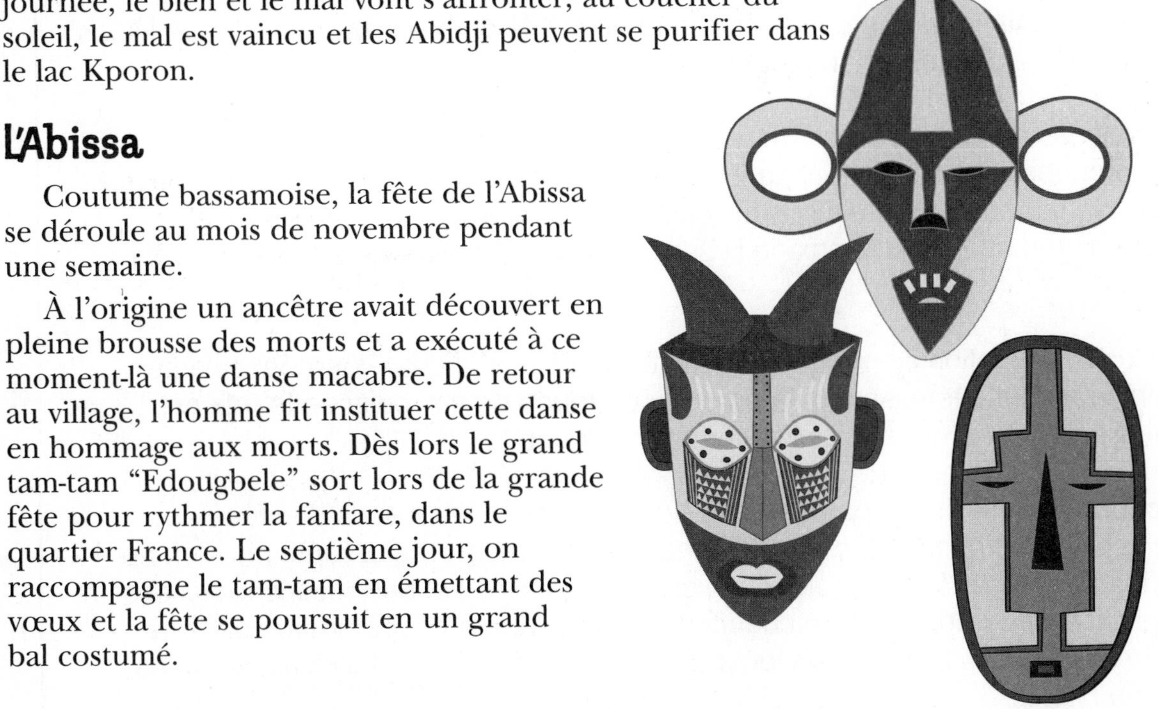

Voyagez en Côte-d'Ivoire

COÛT DE LA VIE

Si le touriste trouvait parfois la vie chère en arrivant à Abidjan, son point de vue a changé depuis la dévaluation. Les prix ayant été sévèrement contrôlés, nul dérapage ne s'est produit et dans les hôtels de catégorie élevée, les prix seront sensiblement les mêmes qu'en France ou moins élevés.

C'est ainsi qu'on trouvera des chambres climatisées avec salle d'eau et sanitaires pour 120 FF : c'est le cas du petit hôtel des Sports, très bien situé au bout de l'ex-rue du Commerce à Abidjan, ou de l'excellent hôtel Kadjona de Korhogo et ils ne sont pas les seuls.

Le prix des repas est variable, mais on trouve fréquemment des plats garnis pour environ 50 FF et moins dans les maquis. Les campeurs et les pique-niqueurs peuvent s'en tirer à bon compte à condition d'acheter uniquement des produits du pays, ce qui n'a pas d'importance; ils sont excellents.

Les transports urbains sont bon marché : les autobus verts d'Abidjan coûtent entre 1,80 FF en ville et 2,80 FF pour la banlieue. La prise en charge des taxis à Abidjan est de 1 FF. A titre indicatif, un trajet de Cocody au Plateau atteint facilement 10 FF. Mais dans les villes de l'intérieur, le tarif est très bas : 1,25 FF la course tant que le périmètre urbain n'est pas dépassé. Quant aux taxis de brousse et autres véhicules interurbains, leurs tarifs changent souvent !

Les locations de voitures sont onéreuses, puisque l'on peut être obligé de choisir une automobile puissante ! A cela il faut ajouter une assurance obligatoire couvrant la voiture, une autre facultative, mais bien utile, concernant le conducteur et les personnes transportées, le prix de l'essence (5,90 FF le litre de super, 3,90 FF le gasoil).

Le prix d'une location de pirogue est élastique. Pour une demi-journée, cela ne devient vraiment intéressant qu'à partir d'un groupe de six, puisque le prix est forfaitaire pour la pirogue mais il faut en trouver une !

Les pourboires n'existent pas dans les hôtels, excepté les pièces données au bagagiste. Théoriquement, c'est la même chose dans les restaurants mais on ne vous les refuse pas ! Lorsqu'on fait un circuit organisé, il est en revanche nécessaire de prévoir un pourboire pour le chauffeur (pour le montant, demander conseil à l'accompagnateur). Il ne faut surtout pas oublier de faire de la monnaie avant de sortir de l'hôtel.

Continents et masses d'eau

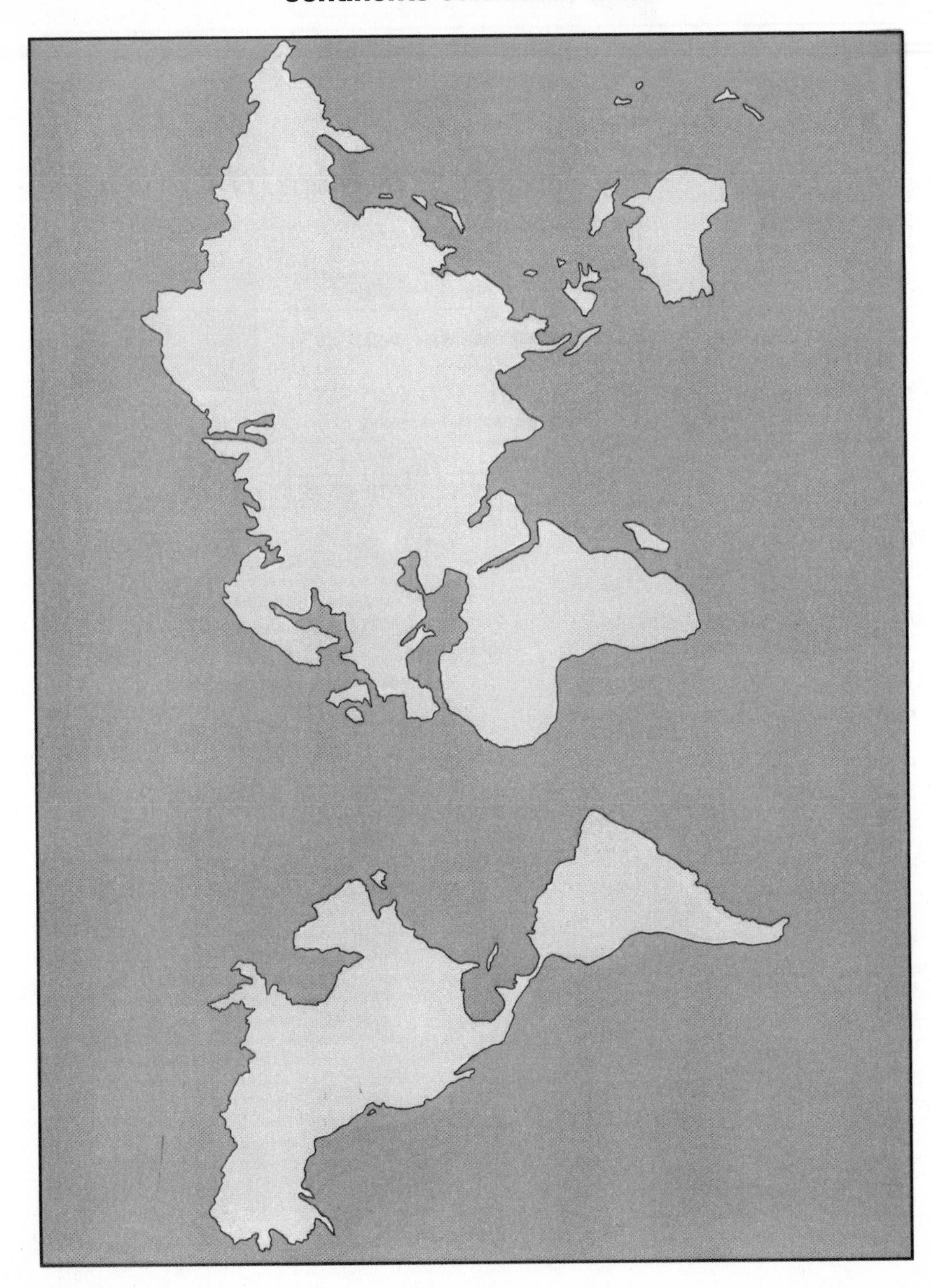

Chartres

Chartres : Identité

Moulin et lavoirs sur les bords de l'Eure

- ✓ **Chef-lieu et ville principale du département d'Eure et Loir (Région : Centre-Val de Loire).**
- ✓ **Indicatifs : administratif, 28 ; postal, 28000 ; téléphone, 02.37 + 6 chiffres.**
- ✓ **Altitude : 170 mètres. Superficie : 1685 hectares.**
- ✓ **Climat océanique modéré. Moyennes des températures : minimales +6°, maximales +14,6°.**

POPULATION

- **42 000 habitants**
  (Chartrains, Chartraines). 60 % de la population a moins de 40 ans ; ce même pourcentage s'applique à la population active.
- **Maire** :
  Jean-Pierre GORGES
- Depuis début 2000, une communauté d'agglomération regroupe **Chartres** et **6 communes périphériques**, (Champhol, Le Coudray, Lèves, Lucé, Luisant, Mainvilliers) avec une population de **87 000 habitants**.

JUMELAGES

Chartres est jumelée avec :
- Ravenne (Italie) depuis 1957
- Spire (Allemagne) depuis 1959
- Chichester (Angleterre) depuis 1959
- Bethleem (Palestine) depuis 1994

Chartres a signé des pactes d'amitié avec :
- Cuzco (Pérou) en 1989
- Sakuraï (Japon) en 1989
- Koursk (Russie)
- Chartres de Bretagne (Ille et Vilaine)

HOTELLERIE ET RESTAURATION

HOTELLERIE
- **En centre ville :**
  - 2 hôtels *** : 101 chambres
  - 4 hôtels **: 203 chambres
  - 2 hôtels non classés : 35 chambres
- **En périphérie :**
  - 1 hôtels *** : 78 chambres
  - 4 hôtels ** : 178 chambres
  - 4 hôtels * : 190 chambres
  - 2 hôtels classés tourisme : 127 chambres
  - 1 hôtel non classé : 70 chambres
  - 1 hôtel en cours de classement : 73 chambres

RESTAURATION
- 5 restaurants classés tourisme : 337 couverts
- 33 restaurants traditionnels : 2 855 couverts

SPECIALITES GASTRONOMIQUES

Chartres offre à ses visiteurs 4 spécialités :
- ✓ **Le pâté de Chartres** : pâté en croûte célèbre dès le 18e siècle.
- ✓ **Le Mentchikoff** : chocolat praliné enrobé de meringue (créé en 1893 pour marquer l'alliance Franco-Russe).
- ✓ **La Poule au Pot** : En souvenir de Henri IV qui fut sacré à Chartres en 1594, un certain nombre de restaurants de la ville proposent la "Poule au Pot" à leurs menus.
- ✓ **Le Cochelin** : Pâtisserie en forme de bonhomme en pâte feuilletée, nature, fourrée au chocolat ou avec de la pâte d'amande, le Cochelin était autrefois confectionnée au moment de la nouvelle année.
- ✓ **La bière de Chartres** : Créée en 1880 par la famille Hornung, la bière de Chartres fut remise au goût du jour en 1999. Cette bière de garde (haut de gamme) est réalisée notamment à partir du blé de Beauce.

Animations organisées par l'Office de Tourisme de Chartres

"Brocantes des quatre saisons"
chaque trimestre
L'Office de Tourisme, en partenariat avec les Antiquaires et Brocanteurs d'Eure-et-Loire, vous propose chaque saison une brocante axée autour d'un thème particulier (l'ecriture, l'art de la table, etc.).

"Fête de l'Eau"
le 9 juin
À la tombée de la nuit, des nageurs aux flambeaux et des canoës-kayaks descendent et illuminent l'Eure, de la Petite Venise à la Place Drouaise. Sur différents ponts de l'Eure, des animations musicales ponctuent la manifestation.

À cette occasion, découvrez **le parcours de sculptures "Au fil de l'eau"** (de mi-avril à octobre).

"Soirées Estivales de Chartres"
du 29 juin au 25 août
Les "Soirées Estivales de Chartres" proposent à 21h15 tous les étés, dans différents sites de la ville, des spectacles gratuits pour le public:

- des concerts et spectacles de rue: les mardis
- des concerts d'orgue: les jeudis (en la Cathédrale)
- du théâtre de rue: les samedis

Rallye touristique "Parcours Estival"
tout l'été
Ce parcours, sous forme de jeu-concours, permet aux touristes et aux Chartrains de découvrir Chartres et ses édifices historiques de façon ludique et originale.

Visite guidée de la ville médiévale
du 1er juillet au 31 août
Découvrez une cité pittoresque qui a su conserver un patrimoine diversifié: de ses maisons à pans de bois, ses vieux ponts jusqu'à la Cathédrale au cœur du cloître médiéval. Visites les mardis, jeudis et samedis, à 14h30. Départ à l'Office de Tourisme. Tarif: 4,57 €; moins de 14 ans: 3,05 €; moins de 6 ans: gratuit.

"Calendrier de l'Avent, Fenêtres ouvertes"
du 1er décembre au 24 décembre
Sur le principe du Calendrier de l'Avent, à partir d'une fenêtre ouverte, différente chaque soir, des animations (contes, chants de Noël, musique, théâtre) vous sont proposées gracieusement entre 18h et 18h30.

Renseignements: Office de Tourisme de Chartres
Tél. 02 37 21 50 00 – Fax 02 37 21 51 91
E-mail: www.chartres-tourisme.com

Plages de Cannes

PLAGES DE LA CROISETTE

LIDO PLAGE
Tél. 04 93 38 25 44 - Fax 04 97 06 54 01
Directeur : M. Fred GIAMMARTINI
€ 11,43 / 27,44
€ 11,43 / 27,44
spécialités italiennes et provençales, poisson

CARLTON BEACH
Tél. 04 93 06 44 94 - Fax 04 93 06 40 25
Directeur : Roberto CAMPONI
E-mail: cepha-beach@interconti.com
€ 27,44 / 44,21
€ 12,96 /67,08
superbe buffet provençal

ZÉNITH PLAGE
Tél. / Fax 04 93 94 03 03
Directeur : Mme Renée GALLIANO
€ 7,62 / 10,67
€ 9,91 / 22,87
poissons frais

EDEN BEACH
Tél. 04 93 94 64 36
Directeur : Bernard BIZEL
€ 7,62 / 10,67
€ 14,94 / 20,58
cuisine traditionnelle

SPORTING PLAGE
Tél. 04 93 43 43 33 - Fax 04 93 00 06 36
Directeur : Christian RABIER
€ 7,62 / 9,15
€ 7,62 / 19,82
salades, spécialités de la mer, langouste, homard

Apprenez le français au cœur de la côte d'Azur!

COURS

Cours Standard
code: CS: 15h par semaine – 9h à 10h30/11h à 12h30

Ce cours constitue une bonne combinaison entre l'écrit et l'oral. Il propose: acquisition de vocabulaire, pratique de la langue et approfondissement des règles grammaticales.

Cours Intensif
code: CI: 25h par semaine; idem + 14h à 16h

L'objectif est de mettre en pratique les connaissances acquises. Programme très complet: cours Standard le matin + 2h l'après-midi où l'accent est mis sur l'expression orale à travers notamment des discussions sur différents thèmes sociaux, culturels.

Cours Super-Intensif
code: CSI: 25h cours Intensif + 5h de cours particuliers par semaine

Programme qui combine des cours collectifs intensifs et des heures de cours particulier. Formule idéale pour approfondir ou préparer de manière individuelle des sujets spécifiques.

HÉBERGEMENT

- En famille d'accueil (demi-pension ou simplement petit déjeuner, chambres simples ou doubles)
- En studio (1 ou 2 personnes)
- En hôtel

CONDITIONS GÉNÉRALES

Pour vous inscrire, vous devez avoir 21 ans.

- Les frais d'inscription sont de 45,73€.
- Réservation des cours: 228,70€.
- Réservation de l'hébergement: 304,89€.

Fiche d'inscription

Inscription
Registration Form
Anmeldeformular
Inscripción

Prénom:

Nom de famille:

Sexe:

Nationalité:

Adresse:

Pays:

Profession:

Date de naissance:

Téléphone:

E-mail:

Cours:

Hébergement:

Date d'arrivée:

Nombre de semaines:

Vous fumez?

Problèmes de santé:

Problèmes

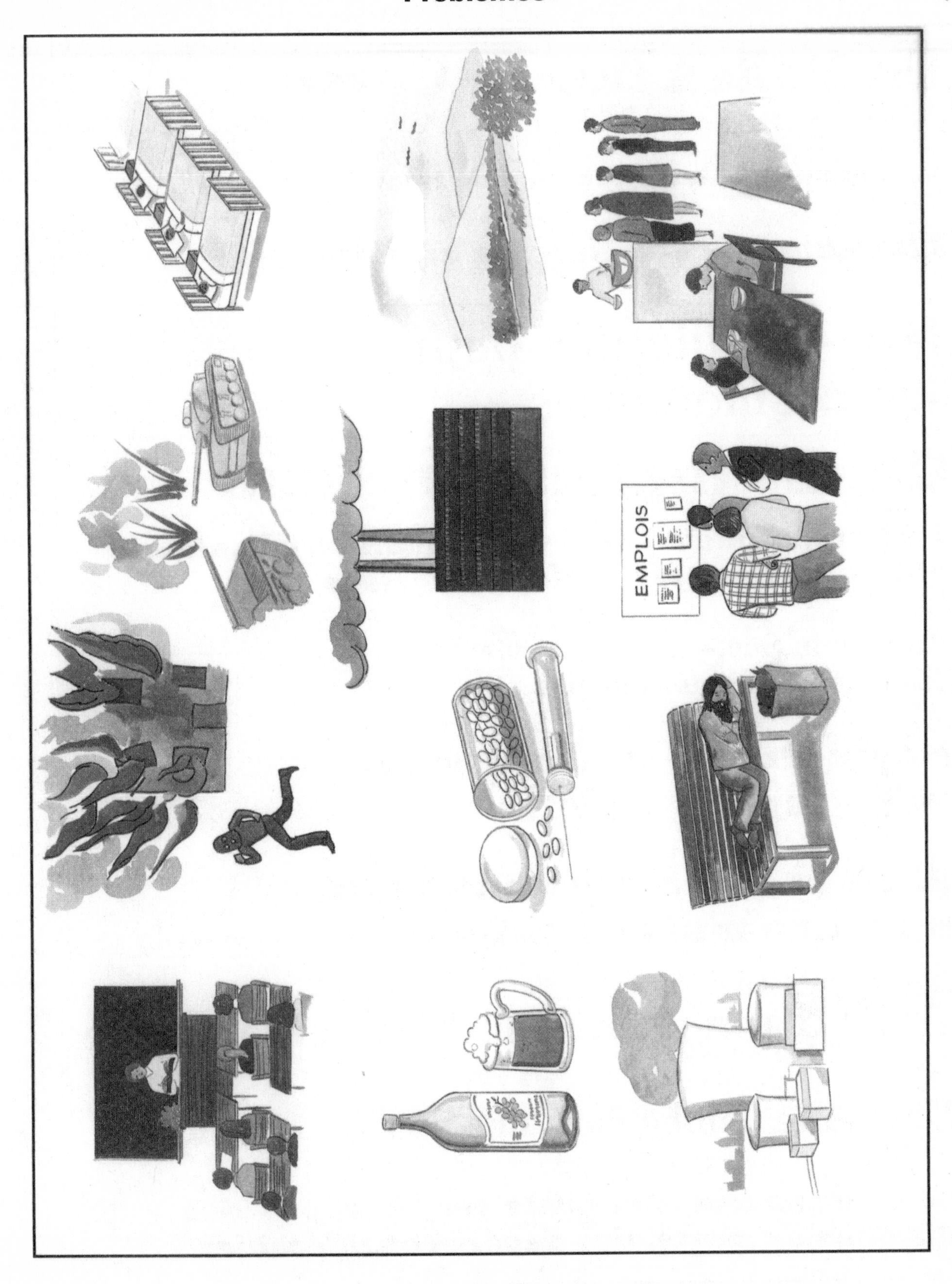

Manchettes

Un Italien tué en Corse

Philippines – la terre continue de trembler

Elle annonce son suicide et disparaît

Mir – inquiétude pour
les cosmonautes

Chirac marque un point

L'informatique à l'école – scandale! Ordinateurs étrangers dans les écoles françaises

Afrique du Sud – le calme revient après
des manifestations violentes

**Moyen-Orient – quel avenir pour
cette région du globe?**

**À 14 ans, il a été condamné
à quatre mois de prison**

Trafic d'armes entre le Liban et la France

Une autre bombe dans une poste à Madrid

Le mauvais temps persiste sur l'Europe – des dizaines de morts, des dégâts considérables

Penser globalement, agir localement
par Antoine, Strasbourg

La Souris Verte

Vous l'aurez compris, nos gouvernements n'arrivent pas à imposer à leurs multinationales bien polluantes une réduction drastique de leurs émissions de gaz à effet de serre, seule solution pour sauver le climat. Encore faut-il qu'ils en aient la volonté!

Loin de ces considérations géopolitiques, vous ne le savez peut-être pas, mais de nombreux gestes quotidiens, faciles, évidents, contribuent à lutter contre l'effet de serre. Montrons-leur que le réchauffement climatique n'est pas une fatalité!

Les transports routiers sont la principale source de gaz à effet de serre. En prenant votre vélo plutôt que votre voiture en ville, vous économisez environ 300g de dioxyde de carbone par kilomètre. Multipliez par le nombre de kilomètres, puis par le nombre d'habitants se déplaçant dans une ville, puis par le nombre de villes... les petits gestes symboliques vont vite prendre de l'ampleur!

On produit également moins de gaz à effet de serre en utilisant les transports en commun plutôt que la voiture, même si la généralisation du ferroutage (camions sur trains) semblerait être la mesure la plus efficace à long terme.

D'autre économies substantielles peuvent être faites en limitant sa consommation d'électricité, de chauffage et d'eau. Par exemple, un kilowatt-heure non consommé (unité relativement petite) épargne en moyenne l'atmosphère de l'émission de 90g d'équivalent-dioxyde de carbone en France. Un mètre cube d'eau non consommé équivaut également à une économie de 100g d'équivalent-dioxyde de carbone: n'oubliez pas qu'il faut pomper l'eau, l'épurer, la distribuer, puis la récupérer et la retraiter... gare aux fuites!

Des gestes quotidiens, donc: éviter le chauffage excessif et le limiter en cas d'absence ou dans les endroits de passage, éteindre systématiquement les lampes et appareils électriques (TV, ordinateurs...) allumés pour rien, utiliser des ampoules basse consommation et autres appareils économes, limiter la capacité des chasses d'eau.

Les déchets non recyclés, et donc incinérés, produisent également du dioxyde de carbone. Pensez ainsi au papier recyclé, à l'autocollant «Pub non merci» sur votre boîte aux lettres, et bien sûr au tri sélectif! Surout, évitez les chaussures à semelles remplies d'air: l'air qu'elles contiennent n'est autre que du SF6, un gaz dont chaque kilogramme contribue autant à l'effet de serre qu'une tonne et demi de dioxyde de carbone.

SIDA

QUE SIGNIFIENT LES QUATRE LETTRES DU MOT SIDA

Les lettres qui composent le mot «sida» définissent la nature de cette maladie :

S pour syndrome, c'est-à-dire l'ensemble des troubles provoqués par la maladie ;

I et **D** pour immunodéficience : le virus atteint les défenses naturelles de l'organisme, qui ne peut plus se protéger contre des infections et risque d'être atteint par diverses maladies dites "opportunistes" et par certains cancers ;

A pour acquise : l'immunodéficience est provoquée par un virus qui pénètre dans l'organisme. Cette immuno-déficience est donc acquise par la personne qui en est atteinte.

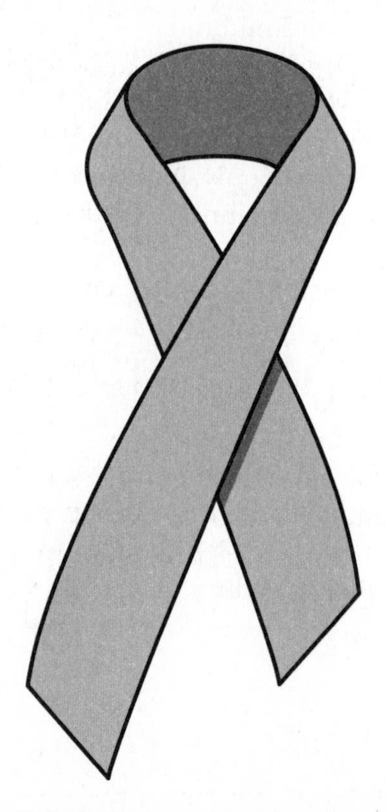

LES DEUX ARMES DE LA LUTTE CONTRE L'ÉPIDÉMIE DE SIDA : LA PRÉVENTION ET LE DIAGNOSTIC/DÉPISTAGE

Le virus qui est la cause du sida s'appelle «Virus de l'Immunodéficience Humaine». Il est souvent désigné par le sigle VIH.

Les traitements et la prise en charge des personnes atteintes ont fait de grands progrès. Dans un grand nombre de cas, ils permettent de prévenir l'évolution vers le sida, mais on ne sait toujours pas guérir l'infection par le VIH. Les deux armes principales restent:

La prévention, qui a pour objectif l'adoption la plus large possible des pratiques qui permettent d'éviter la transmission du virus,

Le diagnostic/dépistage, qui permet à une personne de savoir si elle est atteinte par le VIH et, dans ce cas, de bénéficier le plus tôt possible d'une prise en charge médicale. De plus, quand une personne sait qu'elle est atteinte par le virus, elle est particulièrement sensibilisée à la nécessité d'utiliser les moyens de prévention existants pour éviter de le transmettre.

Taux de chômage par région 2005

Alsace	8,7
Aquitaine	9,7
Auvergne	8,4
Bourgogne	8,5
Bretagne	8,0
Centre	8,6
Champagne-Ardenne	10,2
Corse	10,4
Franche-Comté	8,8
Île-de-France	9,5
Languedoc-Roussillon	13,6
Limousin	7,7
Lorraine	9,9
Midi-Pyrénées	9,8
Nord-Pas-de-Calais	13,3
Basse-Normandie	9,3
Haute-Normandie	10,8
Pays de la Loire	8,1
Picardie	10,9
Poitou-Charentes	9,4
Provence-Alpes-Côte d'Azur	11,7
Rhône-Alpes	8,5

Expressions de la route

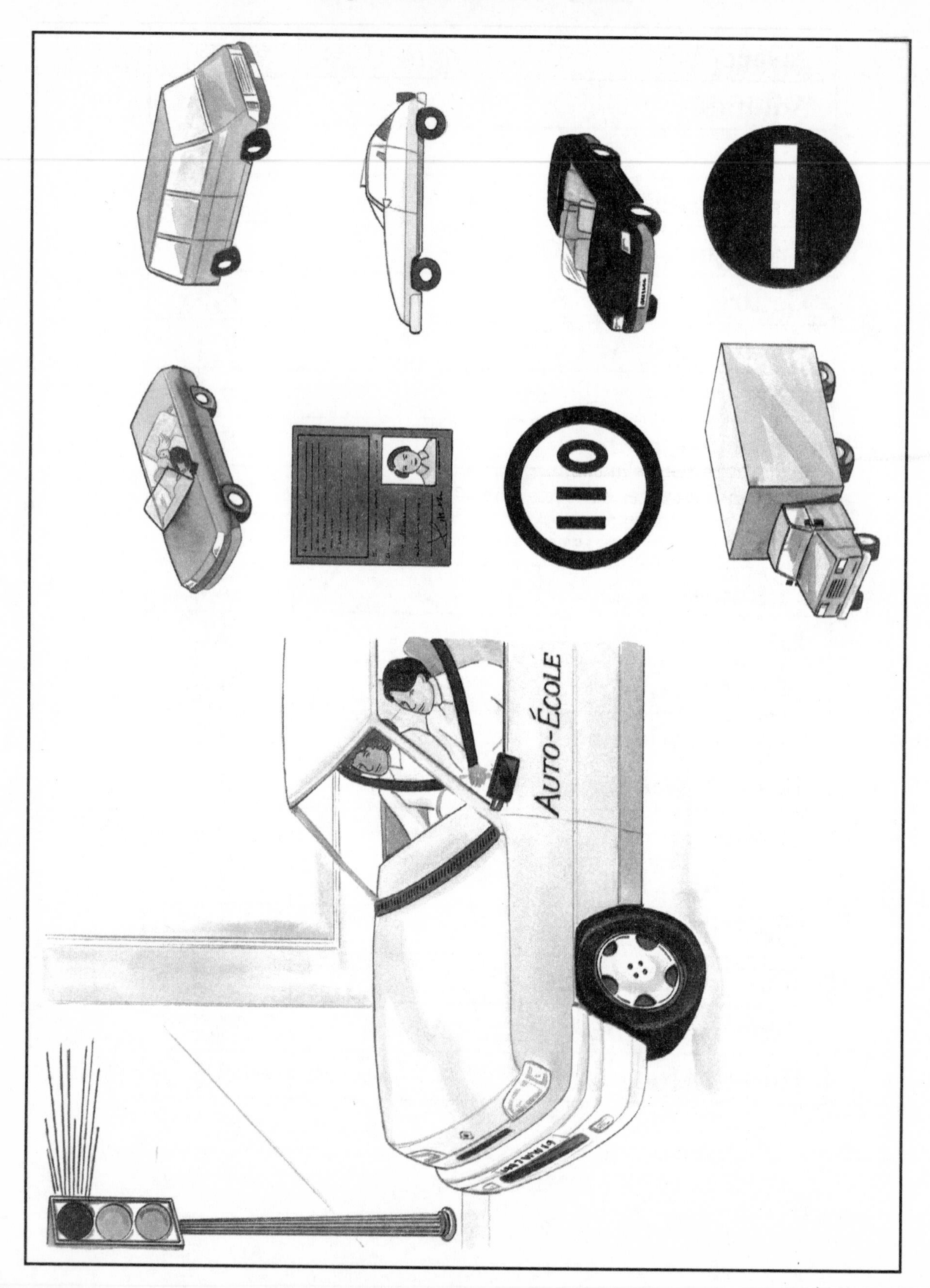

Catégories de permis

Type de véhicules	Age/Permis	
Motocyclette légère: cylindrée limitée à 125 cm3. Équivalence avec le Permis A1.	16 ans 20 ans depuis 2 ans	A1 B
Motocyclette: puissance limitée à 34 cv (25 Kw). Accès après deux ans à toutes les motocyclettes. **Motocyclette:** toutes cylindrées.	18/21 ans	A
Tricycle et quadricycle à moteur	16 ans	B1
Voiture, fourgonnette, camionnette: véhicules automobiles ayant un poids total autorisé en charge (PTAC) qui n'excède pas 3 500 kg, affectés au transport de personnes et comportant, outre le siège du conducteur, huit places assises maximum, ou affectés au transport de marchandises. Une remorque d'un PTAC de 750 kg maximum peut être attelée.	18 ans	B
Transport en commun: véhicule automobile affecté au transport de personnes comportant plus de huit places assises outre le siège du conducteur. Une remorque d'un PTAC de 750 kg maximum peut être attelée.	21 ans	D
Véhicule B + remorque: Véhicule attelé d'une remorque de plus de 750 kg, lorsque le PTAC de la remorque est supérieur au poids à vide du véhicule tracteur ou lorsque le total des PTAC (véhicule + remorque) est supérieur à 3 500 kg.	18 ans	E (b)
Véhicule C + remorque: ensemble de véhicules couplés dont le véhicule tracteur entre dans la catégorie C et la remorque excède 750 kg de PTAC.	18 ans	E (c)
Véhicule D + remorque: ensemble de véhicules couplés don't le véhicule tracteur entre dans la catégorie D et la remorque excède 750 kg de PTAC.	21 ans	E (d)
Cyclomoteur: cylindrée limitée à 49 cm3 (Scooter, mobylette)	14 ans	BSR

Test du Code de la Route

En tournant à gauche au prochain carrefour,

- ❑ je serai sur une route à caractère prioritaire.
- ❑ je vais quitter une route à caractère prioritaire.

Le conducteur de la voiture grise doit laisser passer le piéton.

- ❑ Oui
- ❑ Non

Test du Code de la Route

Ce panneau indique que cette voie est interdite à tous les véhicules dont la longueur dépasse 10 m.

❑ Oui
❑ Non

Pour rouler avec ce véhicule,

❑ je dois dégager toute la neige sur le véhicule.
❑ je dois dégager la neige de toute les vitres.
❑ je dois dégager la neige du pare-brise avant.

Twingo de Renault

Plus d'un tour dans son sac

Twingo a toujours un rangement en réserve. A l'avant, à l'arrière, dans la boîte à gants, sous le volant, dans les portières.

La banquette arrière coulisse et se rabat. Vous pouvez ainsi privilégier l'espace pour les passagers ou agrandir le volume du coffre jusqu'à 1096 dm3. Elle possède la modularité d'un monospace et le gabarit d'un "minispace."

Votre confort fait l'objet de toutes ses attentions. Accéder à l'arrière, rien de plus facile, les sièges avant basculent d'un doigt. Son ouverture d'esprit égale la largeur de ses portes.

L'assurance de votre sérénité

Twingo vous sera fidèle très longtemps. Elle bénéficie de **la garantie 12 ans anti corrosion** et nécessite peu d'entretien. Vous pouvez rouler tranquille, la vidange n'intervient que tous les 20 000 km et le remplacement des bougies tous les 60 000 km.

Twingo respecte l'environnement. Elle est dotée d'un filtre à huile écologique à cartouche recyclable. Le 1.2 16V adopte une nouvelle architecture et intègre de nouveaux matériaux tels que le plastique. Il est donc allégé et plus de 95% de son poids est recyclable.

Plus d'un tour dans son sac

Twingo se met en quatre pour vous faciliter la vie.

Voulez-vous rouler en rythme? Juste derrière le volant, **le satellite de commande radio** met la musique à portée de votre main (selon version).

Vous ne quittez plus la route des yeux. Son **système de navigation par satellite** (en option selon versions) intégré à l'autoradio vous guide vocalement, comme un véritable copilote. Enfin le siège conducteur réglable en hauteur (selon version) vous permet d'adopter une position de conduite idéale.

Signalisation routière internationale

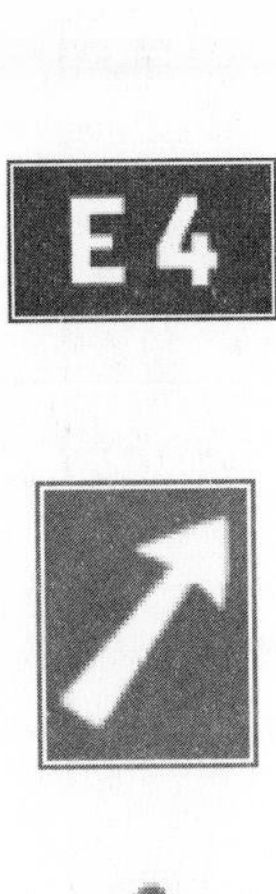

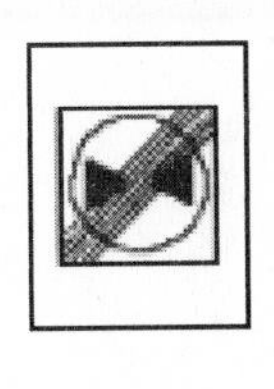

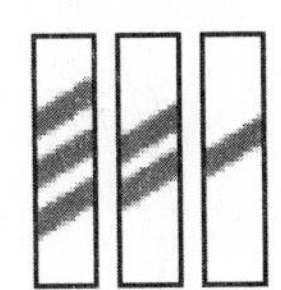

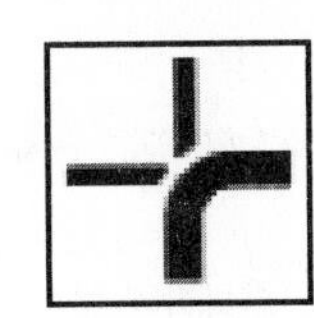

À la station-service I

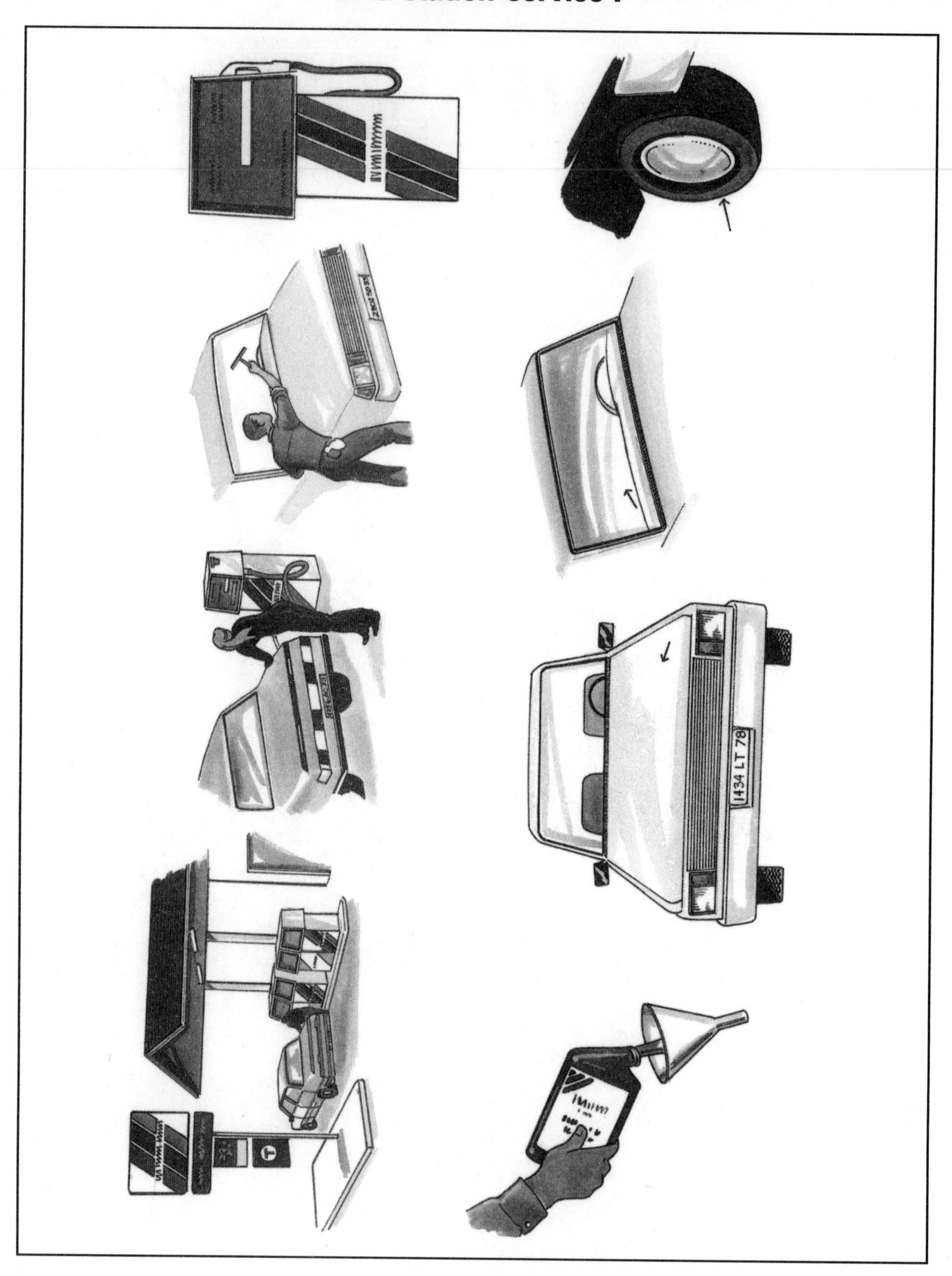

Parties de la voiture

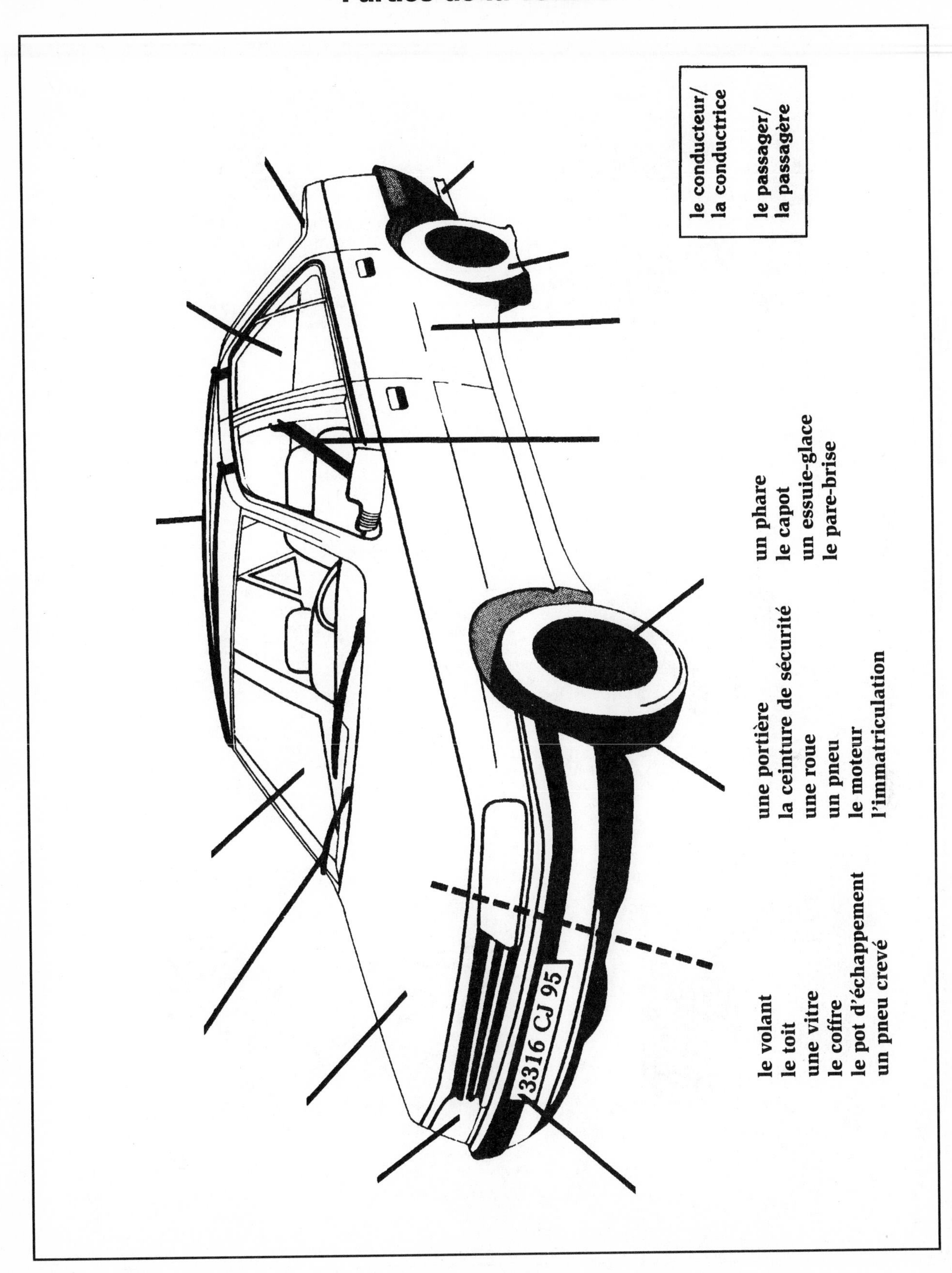

À la station-service II

Carte TOTAL Le Club

Carte TOTAL Le Club

•••••••• Elle récompense votre fidélité et vous offre en plus une assistance dépannage gratuite

TOTAL Le Club

•15 jours d'assistance dépannage même en bas de chez vous.

Avec la carte TOTAL Le Club, vous cumulez bien sûr vos points cadeaux à chaque plein de carburant (10 litres = 1 point) mais vous bénéficiez également de 15 jours d'assistance gratuite après chaque plein effectué dans une station service TOTAL en France (30 litres minimum).
L'assistance du Club TOTAL couvre tous les risques de panne immobilisant le véhicule (même en bas de chez vous) y compris crevaison, perte de clés, panne d'essence, erreur de prise de carburant (hors accidents et panne d'alarme).

Pour en bénéficier, faites créditer votre carte TOTAL Le Club au moment du paiement de votre plein de carburant.

En cas de panne, il vous suffit simplement d'appeler Le Club grâce au numéro figurant au dos de votre carte et de présenter votre carte TOTAL Le Club au dépanneur.

Des cadeaux **Plus** l'Assistance Dépannage **Plus** la Souplesse de paiement

Garage

CARROSSERIE SAYO
32, Rue de la République
33310 LORMONT

Plus de 50 années d'experience à votre service

Réparation automobiles toutes marques

Agréée par les Compagnies d'Assurance

Prêt d'un véhicule pendant la durée de la réparation (suivant nos disponibilités)

Pose de Pare-Brise

Contrôle de Train Avant

Membre du GNCR

Pour votre reparation, nous disposons de tous les équipements nécessaires:

Tel. 05 56 06 39 53
Fax 05 56 74 27 10

E-mail:
carrosseriejeansayo@wanadoo.fr

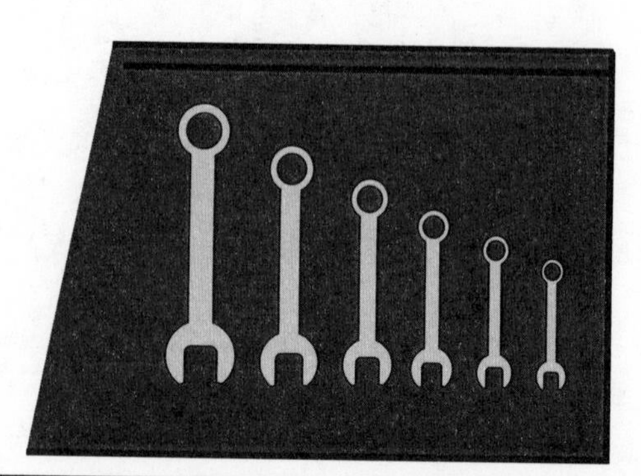